ALL SORTS OF
SORTS 3

**Primary, Standards-Based,
Content Area Vocabulary Sorts
In Science, Social Studies, Math and Health**

by Sheron Brown

A Teaching Resource Center Publication

Published by
Teaching Resource Center

P.O. Box 82777, San Diego, CA 92138
1-800-833-3389
www.trcabc.com

Edited by Laura Woodard

PRINTED IN THE UNITED STATES OF AMERICA ISBN:1-56785-064-2

Table of Contents

Introduction

Teaching content area vocabulary at the primary levels is always a daunting task. The teacher has to take each student's prior knowledge, reading ability, word attack skills and understanding of the content area into consideration. After evaluating all of the above, the teacher must devise a way to teach the content area concepts along with the related vocabulary words. The vocabulary and concept sorts in this book were designed to enhance and support the teacher's efforts to instruct his/her students in both content area vocabulary development and the content area concepts as well. The sorts were designed to meet the national standards in science, social studies, math and health education.

Using the Sorts *Prior to Instruction* in a Content Area

You may use the vocabulary sorts in this book as an assessment device prior to presenting the content area unit. You may choose to use either an open or closed sort for each student's initial assessment. **Before using any sort, always make sure the students can read the words in the sort.** You can do this by having the students point to the sort words while you read them aloud, one column at a time. Have the students repeat each sort word after you say it. Placing the students in small cooperative groups or with a partner to do the sort together is another way to support the struggling readers in the classroom. You may start by making a transparency of the sort, cutting it apart, and doing a whole-group sort with teacher and student input using the overhead projector. You may leave the completed sample sort on the overhead for the students to use as a reference point as they do their own sorts at their desks.

It is recommended that the sort cards be kept in the large freezer-type baggies. These baggies are durable, resealable and have large openings for easily removing the cards. The students'

names should also be written on each baggie with a permanent marker. If students have three-ring binders, the freezer baggies may be three-hole punched and the sort cards and category markers kept in their binders throughout the unit of study.

After the students cut out the sort cards, instruct them to **use a marker or crayon to "border" the category marker cards.** This makes it easy to find the category cards in the baggie without having to look through all of the cards.

Assessment via an Open Sort

In order to determine the extent of a student's prior knowledge for the vocabulary or unit concepts not yet presented, pass out the selected vocabulary sort without the category cards at the top. Instruct the students to organize the sort words into any categories they "see." An open sort provides a window into the students' thinking. Observe how they choose to organize their sort words into categories. After an agreed upon time, ask the students to share the ways they chose to sort their word cards. Be accepting of any categories the students "saw" in the words. List the students' categories on the board or overhead projector and discuss the reasons they sort the words into these categories. After determining how many of the students "saw" the intended groupings for the sort, you can decide how much or how little instruction will be needed for that particular content area or for word sorting in general.

After teaching a specific unit, you may use an open sort as a summative assessment device. Using just the sort cards, instruct the students to sort them into any categories they "see." The teacher can simply observe how many students correctly organized the sort cards. Depending on your observation, you may elect to do more instruction on that specific unit, or you may move on to a new unit of instruction.

Assessment Via a Closed Sort

A closed sort may also be used as an assessment vehicle prior to instruction in a particular unit of study. Pass out the entire sort **including the category markers** and instruct the students to place the category cards at the top of their desks. Again, orally read all of the sort cards to ensure all of the students are reading them correctly, and have them repeat each word after you. Observing how many sort cards have been placed under their correct categories provides you with some insight into how much or how little the students already know about the particular sort concept(s). You can then set some instructional timeframes for that particular unit based on your observations of the closed sort results.

A closed sort may also be used as a **"unit test"** after a particular content area unit has been presented. Pass out the entire sort and instructs the students to place the category markers at the top of their desks. If there are word cards containing vocabulary you chose not to use during the unit of study, instruct the students to remove those word cards before during the sort. You may observe how many students have organized the sort cards under the correct categories. You could also have the students copy the entire closed sort onto a blank sheet of paper as a formal "written" assessment. Again, based on how many students complete the word sort correctly, you may review the unit material previously taught, or move on to a new unit of study.

Using the Sorts as a Part of Instruction

The sorts can be used as a part of content area instruction. The sorts easily lend themselves to a "hands-on" lesson, complete with evidence from the students' textbooks or research as to why each word card has been placed under a particular category. Sorting the word cards could be a small group activity with the students then "sharing out" to the rest of the class how they sorted their cards and why. Because these sorts are designed for primary students with limited reading abilities, the emphasis in this book is solely on helping build the primary students' sight recognition of important content area vocabulary words and standards-based concepts they represent. At no time should primary students be expected to correctly spell all of the words included in a sort; you might want to select some of the important words that are harder to spell, for example Atlantic Ocean or United States, and present them prior to the assessment as important words to learn to spell.

HERE ARE SOME SUGGESTIONS FOR USING THE SORTS DURING A COURSE OF STUDY.

- About a week before beginning a unit, make flashcards of the vocabulary words you wish to have your students learn for the new unit. Depending on the students' prior knowledge and the amount of new vocabulary words you have decided upon, introduce **no more than three to five new words each day**. Place the flashcards in a pocket chart or on a bulletin board with the new unit's title as a heading. As you introduce each vocabulary word, have the students repeat it after you. Give a short definition of each word or ask for student definitions. Each day, add up to five more words to the pocket chart or bulletin board and review the previous day's word cards. This purpose of this exercise is to add new content area words to your students' sight vocabularies and not to teach their definitions. Tying together the words with their meanings will be the focus of the new unit of study. By looking at the new vocabulary words and reinforcing sight recognition in the previous week, your students will be much more comfortable when meeting the same words in context in their content area textbooks and in their word sorts.

- Introduce the sort words and category markers on a transparency using an overhead projector. Cut out the category cards and border them with a colored overhead pen so you can easily spot them during sorting activities. Model reading the sort words and giving the reasons each word card belongs under its particular category marker. You might ask for student input while the class or the group is watching you sort the word cards. Save the cut-up transparency for another modeled lessons, including having your students watch you do a "speed sort" while you are being timed. Afterwards you can place the cut-up transparency at a learning center where the students can sort it on the overhead projector as an independent activity.

• Break the students into small, heterogeneously mixed groups. Ask each group to find all of the sort cards that go under **one** of the sort's categories. You can also instruct the groups to **add one or two more words of their own** to the category. They can share these additional words with the rest of the class. As the students in each group share out their words, they should present their reasoning and/or evidence from their textbooks that helped them decide to place the word cards in the selected category. These words could also be posted in a pocket chart, on a bulletin board or on a piece of butcher paper along with other vocabulary words from the unit of study.

• Students can keep a "Content Area Notebook" in which they write down the sorts. Have them use two facing pages in their notebooks for one content area sort. In that way, they will have additional room on the pages to write observations and generalizations about the concepts they have learned in each unit of study. See page VIII for more about the Content Area Notebook.

• After the specific unit of study is finished, students can glue the sort cards under the correct category cards on a sheet of construction paper or legal-size paper. This is a good center project or homework assignment.

Using *Speed Sorts* to Increase Student Proficiency with Content Area Words and Concepts

The speed sort format lends itself to increasing word recognition along with concept understanding. It provides for multiple interactions with the category cards and the word cards. A speed sort is exactly what its name implies: how fast can you sort the word cards under their correct categories? Students love to race against the clock, the egg timer, each other, other groups or even the teacher as they quickly sort their word cards. It is through the multiple opportunities of interacting with the words and the category markers that students will increase their sight word vocabularies along with their concept knowledge. However, **students should not be asked to do a speed sort unless they have done at least one or two closed sorts** with their category cards and word cards. They must have some familiarity with the categories and the word cards before they are asked to use them in a speed sort.

HOW TO DO A SPEED SORT

Make sure your students understand these steps and guidelines when doing a speed sort:
1. Begin by placing the category cards at the top of your desks. Place the word sort cards in a pile, **face down**, in the center of your desks.
2. Wait until a signal has been given, then turn over your word cards and begin the speed sort.
3. When you finish the speed sort, **raise your hand**. Anyone who shouts out is automatically disqualified. The teacher will say, "Stop." All students are to stop sorting and **raise both hands** while the teacher checks the sort of the student who was first to raise his or her hand.
4. If the student has done the sort correctly, the teacher announces it and writes the winning time on the board or overhead along with the student's name. If the sort has been done incorrectly, the teacher tells the class to continue the sort until someone completes it correctly.
5. The students are then challenged to "beat" the winning time.

Further Suggestions for Using Speed Sorts

- There is nothing students like better than to "beat the teacher," speed sorts included! Make an overhead transparency of the sort you are currently using and cut out the category markers and the word cards. Place the category markers at the top of the overhead and set a timer. Have the students say, "Go!" and begin sorting the word cards on the overhead. You can think aloud as you go, modeling how to sort the words under the correct categories. It goes without saying that you should take longer normal to do the sort so the entire class has the opportunity to "beat" the teacher's time. Write your time on the board or overhead and challenge the students to beat it.

- Egg timers are a great speed sort device, since the students are working to beat the egg timer instead of each other. They are available in kitchen supply departments and are available in different minute increments. Five- and six-minute egg timers can also be placed in a word study center for small group speed sorts that can be done independently. One student can be the "checker" and be in charge of the answer keys (found in the appendix). The same rules hold true for the students doing the sorts independently at a word study center as for a whole-group speed sort. After one speed sort has been completed and verified by the checker, someone else in the group becomes the checker, and the process begins all over again. Egg timers have additional benefits for teachers in that they don't need batteries, and they don't make any noise!

- Speed sorting is a great activity for a parent volunteer or instructional aide to do with students who need more time and support in recognizing and categorizing the word cards. It is a fun format that is easy to explain and set up. The practice it provides, especially for the struggling readers in the class, supports their word and concept acquisition without the students really being aware they're having "practice sessions." The students can keep a record of how long it took them to do the word sorts. Because of the additional practice the speed sorts provide, they will see their times drop, which is a motivational aspect of the speed sorts.

- As a homework project, the students can take the sort cards home in baggies and have parents time them as they complete the sorts. Because of the unique format, parents are generally very supportive of word sorting activities. They can actually see their children learning the words and concepts as they sort.

- Some primary classrooms have upper grade "buddies" who come to visit the younger students and support their learning. Having the upper grade student do speed sorts with his or her primary grade buddy is an excellent activity to help foster a positive relationship. The upper grade student can provide the one-on-one support the primary student may need to do the speed sorts. The older student can hold the answer key and keep track of the primary student's times.

Using *Blind Sorts* to Increase Student Proficiency with Content Area Words and Concepts

A blind sort reinforces that reading and learning words and concepts is also an auditory process. Students listen for the words to be pronounced by the teacher and then hold up the category marker, raise their hands or in some other way signal the category that matches each word or phrase.

Using *Blind Sorts* as an Assessment Device and as a Proficiency Activity

- You can easily see how well the students have learned the sort concepts by how many students identify the correct categories.
- You can isolate the category or word patterns your students need to review. Present the categories for additional instruction, drill and practice. You can also use the blind sort to determine which individual students need additional instruction. You might want to place these students in a small word study group for further instruction and practice.
- The blind sort is a unique type of sort that does not involve any paper and pencil. The students must learn to use their auditory skills in concert with their understanding of the categories to make a judgment as to where each spoken word or phrase belongs.

Using *Writing Sorts* to Increase Student Proficiency with Content Area Words and Concepts

A writing sort is a more challenging version of the traditional "Friday Spelling Test." In this most difficult of all the sorts, the students are not only asked to correctly spell words found in the sort, but also to place those words in their correct categories.

Direct students to fold a sheet of paper into as many columns as there are categories in the sort. Have them head each column with one of the sort categories. Select one of the sort words from each category to act as a "key word." Dictate the key word and spell it for the students. The students write each key word under its correct category. The key word provides a reminder as to which kinds of words belong in each column. Then select about two to three words from each category and randomly call them out for the students to write under their correct categories, with the correct spelling.

The vocabulary and concept words included in these sorts are quite challenging for primary students to correctly spell. Highlighting an important content area word or two from each category for your students to learn to spell is a valuable way to support their vocabulary growth. Focusing on sight recognition of these important words while instructing your students in the concepts they represent is a much more valuable use of time than insisting they learn to correctly spell all the words in the sort.

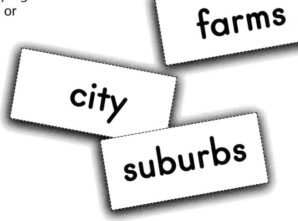

Glossary of Word Sort Terms

1. **open sort** – The teacher provides only the words, and the students decide the sort categories based on what they see. Open sorts are valuable as they provide a window for the teacher into each student's word work and which features they are noticing or not noticing.

2. **closed sort** – The teacher provides the categories for the word sort. Closed sorts are used more frequently than open sorts, as they allow the teacher to focus students' attention on a word feature, characteristic or pattern the class is currently studying. Closed sorts are also valuable assessment tools. The teacher can rapidly assess student understanding of word features by simply checking the students' sorts against the Answer Keys (pages 170-189).

3. **speed sort** – This is usually a timed sort that students can do once they are adept at sorting words. Speed sorts are excellent for building fluency and accuracy when working with known patterns and concepts. Students can record the time it takes to sort a given set of words and then try to beat their records.

4. **blind sort** – This is a closed sort in which the teacher calls out the words and the students point to or say the categories they see listed on the worksheet or written on the board or overhead. Blind sorts are particularly useful when the teacher wants to focus on the sound patterns rather than the visual patterns of the words.

5. **writing sort** – The students have key words, provided by the teacher, written as column headers. They write words under the appropriate categories as the teacher calls them out, using the key words as spelling guides. Writing sorts focus on both auditory and visual patterns in words and are a combination of closed and blind sorts.

6. **OUT OF SORTS** – These are words that have been included with the sorts but do not fit into any of the categories. They serve as an extra contrast and challenge for students who already understand word sorting.

Word Sorting Management Suggestions

- Large group, small group, word study center, and individual activities take time and organization and can be somewhat noisy. Take the time to decide how you want your word sorting sessions to run. Are you going to do the sorts at the beginning of class or at the end? What will your seating be? What materials will you need for your chosen word study activities? How will you organize your materials? How will the students organize theirs? Have a clear picture in your mind of how you see the word study sessions functioning. If you are clear, then your students will be clear as well.

- The students can record the completed content area sorts in their Content Area Notebooks. A table of contents should be a part of this notebook. Completing the table of contents is a teacher-directed activity with primary students. It will help in the organization of their vocabulary work and will also help in holding students accountable for their work. Present a model of how you want each notebook page set up. Have the students put their work on facing pages in the notebook to provide enough room for the vocabulary words and other additional activities.

- Large freezer-type baggies are very durable and can hold each week's word sort cards in students' desks or in organizational containers. Have each student write his or her name on the baggie with a permanent marker. At the end of the week students can glue the sorts on paper as a review task for Thursday night's homework before the Friday assessment or while another group is being assessed on their words by the teacher.

- Plan to spend a few weeks or more (depending on the grade level) training your students in the different word sort formats and activities you have decided to use in your classroom. Use words/letters that the entire class can read so they can truly focus on how to do the activity and not the words.

- Cutting apart the sort cards takes time, especially for the little ones! Monday morning while taking attendance and getting the week started is a great time to have students cut the cards apart. Parent volunteers can also help in cutting up the sorts. **Train your students to mark their word sort cards by writing their initials on the back of each card.** Then, when students are doing cooperative word activities, the cards can easily be returned to their owners' baggies.

- Stick to your format. Keep the word study segments crisp, focused and organized. Realize that each word sort activity will take a while until the students really learn the procedures. After that, many of the word study activities are independent or for partners. You are then free to observe and to work with individual students or small groups of students who need additional support.

- Use a cut-up transparency on the overhead projector to introduce the sort's vocabulary and concepts. You can model the sort while you are scooting the words around on the overhead. Competing to beat the teacher's time in a "speed sort" is a great incentive for students.

- Use the blank templates in the *All Sorts of Sorts* books to tailor your word choices for your students who may need more challenges or more practice with a particular set of concepts. Allow older students to formulate word sorts based on the current unit of study, in which they supply half of the words for the sort and you supply the other half.

- Don't ignore the possibilities of using word sorts to review concepts and vocabulary in other curricular areas. Word sorts can be used in an infinite number of ways throughout the curriculum to practice, review, and assess vocabulary and concepts being taught.

Suggested Management System for Working with Two Groups of Students

An organizational template for working with two small groups of students is given below. On the first day working with a new sort, the teacher meets with the students who need more teacher support. While the teacher is meeting with this group, the more capable students try to tackle the new sort independently via a closed sort, using an answer key to check their work. Notice that there are suggestions for many different kinds of word study activities that will provide the necessary "multiple opportunities" for your students to interact with the new vocabulary words during the unit of study.

WORD STUDY GROUP SCHEDULES

Note: It is assumed that content area units usually take longer than a week. The two-group schedule given in this format may certainly be "stretched out" to include a unit that lasts far longer!

GROUP I

DAY 1:
Time: 15 minutes
Teacher Lead Activity

Introduce the concept of the word sort based on assessment data and/or the content area currently being studied. Do an open sort first, and then lead the students directly into a closed sort. Lead students to make generalizations about the words and the categories they belong to. Review the teaching points of the word sort. Put the sort away.

DAY 2:
Time: 15-20 minutes
Independent Activity

Students do the closed sort again and copy it into their word study books. They formulate and write any generalizations or understandings they may have at this point. Put the sort away.

DAY 3:
Independent Activity

Students do partner or group speed sorts to gain fluency and vocabulary recognition. One student can act as the "timer," or students can time themselves against the clock. Students begin word hunts for additional words to match the sort categories. They add the words to their word study books or to a class chart to be discussed by the group. Put the sort away.

DAY 4:
Independent Activity

Ideas for Exploring Other Word Forms
1. Create word configuration boxes for the other forms of the sort words using graph paper. Students print one letter of the word into each graph box and then outline the shape of the word using the graph lines and a crayon or marking pen.
2. Write a paragraph using as many of the sort words or their other word forms as possible. Select a few to share with the class.
3. Create a crossword puzzle using the sort words. Share with the class as a review device.
4. Play a word sort game with two players using an open-ended game board. One student can be the "checker" and hold the answer key.
5. Do S-A-W with the word sort words. **Sort** the word cards according to their categories, put the words category into **alphabetical** order, and then **write** the words on a separate sheet of paper.
6. Practice in partners via an oral sorting pre-test before Friday's "formal assessment."

DAY 5:
Assessment

Assessment can take many different forms:
• Teacher-directed formal spelling test using only one to two of the vocabulary words from each sort category.
• A "writing sort" in which the students not only are asked to correctly spell one or two words from each category, but must also place those "spelling" words under their correct categories.

- Oral test in partners, with one partner checking the sort using the answer keys found in the appendix.
- Cloze sentences (fill in the blanks) that illustrate each word's meaning or concept. Students may use their sort cards to check the correct spelling of the words.

GROUP 2

DAY 1:
Time: 15 minutes
Independent Group Work

Introduce the concept of the word sort based on assessment data and/or the content area unit currently being studied. Do an open sort first and then lead the students directly into a closed sort. Lead students to make generalizations about the words and their correct categories. Review the teaching points of the word sort. Put the sort away.

DAY 2:
Time: 15-20 minutes
Independent Activity

Students do the closed sort again and copy it into their word study books. They formulate and write any generalizations or understandings they may have noticed. Put the sort away.

DAY 3:
Independent Activity

Students do partner or group speed sort to gain fluency and vocabulary recognition. One student can act as the "timer" or students can time themselves against the clock. Students begin word hunts for additional words to match the sort categories. They add the words to their word study books or to a class chart to be discussed by the group. Put the sort away.

DAY 4
Independent Activity

Choices for Exploring Other Word Forms
1. Create word configuration boxes for the other forms of the sort words using graph paper. Students print one letter of the word into each graph box and then outline the shape of the word using the graph lines and a crayon or marking pen.
2. Write a paragraph using as many of the sort words or their other word forms as possible. Select a few to share with the class.
3. Create a crossword puzzle using the sort words. Share with the class as a review device.
4. Play a word sort game with two players using an open-ended game board. One student can be the "checker" and hold the answer key.
5. Do S-A-W with the word sort words. **Sort** the word cards according to their categories, put the words category into **alphabetical** order, and then **write** the words on a separate sheet of paper.
6. Practice in partners via an oral sorting pre-test before Friday's "formal assessment."

DAY 5:
Assessment

Assessment can take many different forms:
- Teacher-directed formal spelling test using only one to two of the vocabulary words from each sort category.
- A "writing sort" in which the students not only are asked to correctly spell one or two words from each category, but must also place those "spelling" words under their correct categories.
- Oral test in partners, with one partner checking the sort using the answer keys found in the appendix.
- Cloze sentences (fill in the blanks) that illustrate each word's meaning or concept. Students may use their sort cards to check the correct spelling of the words.

Note: It is assumed that content area units usually take longer than a week. The two group schedule given in this format may certainly be "stretched out" to include a unit study lasting far longer!

A Final Note

In researching the specific content for the vocabulary sorts contained in All Sorts of Sorts 3, both national and state content standards were used.

The National Council for the Social Studies, the primary membership organization in the social studies field, organized a standards task force in 1993 and formally adopted the social studies standards document in 1994. Dissemination to social studies educators throughout the country began in 1994, and continues to this day. Ten themes form the framework within the social studies standards which stress overall curriculum design and comprehensive student performance expectations.

The National Science Education Standards contain a complete set of outcomes for students to know, understand and be evaluated on in grades K – 12 in the area of science. There are eight categories of science content standards ranging from physical, life, earth and space, science and technology, to science as inquiry, personal and social perspectives, and the history and nature of science.

In the area of mathematics, the National Council of Teachers of Mathematics has developed mathematical standards based on both content and processes. The ten mathematics standards, as with those in science and social studies, are not separate topics for study, but represent carefully integrated strands designed to support the learning of connected mathematical ideas. The standards of the various content areas used as the basis for this Sorts 3 book should be explored and used as ways to develop and enhance students' knowledge and performance.

living things

non-living things

cat	tree
ball	hen
dog	duck
fish	snake
hat	lamp
pen	TV
pig	desk
cow	book
rug	fox
box	pin

plants	animals

- -

tree	grass
fox	fern
dog	fruit
flower	seed
deer	pig
rose	puppy
bush	leaf
daisy	stem
chick	cow
kitten	cat

plants	animals	OUT OF SORTS

- -

deer	tree
daisy	desk
cactus	grass
tiger	fox
bike	beaver
bear	computer
squirrel	petunia
shrub	pig
fern	tulip
lion	hamster

belongs to plants	belongs to animals

leaf	seed
fur	flower
paws	fruit
stem	eyes
branches	petals
teeth	roots
thorn	nose
pollen	legs
claws	mouth
ears	heart

parts of plants	parts of animals

- -

seedling	flower
head	fur
eyes	thorn
stem	leaf
paws	ears
roots	seed
branches	lungs
teeth	nose
mouth	pollen
seed coat	stomach

belongs to plants	belongs to animals	OUT OF SORTS

leaf	tail
nose	branches
eyes	fur
seed	ears
door	buds
flower	roof
stem	seed coat
window	pollen
roots	lungs
paws	heart

vertebrates (have backbones)	**invertebrates** (do not have backbones)

dog	rattlesnake
jellyfish	crab
spider	snail
cat	tiger
parrot	bear
worm	squid
shrimp	frog
bee	lobster
whale	fox
fly	elephant

vertebrates (have backbones)	invertebrates (do not have backbones)	OUT OF SORTS

snake	cow
snail	bee
shark	spider
rock	eagle
earthworm	garter snake
wolf	horse
flower	carrot
slug	ticks
dolphin	tree
panda bear	lion

mammals	reptiles

- -

deer	rattlesnake
elephant	dog
coral snake	cat
camel	tree frog
turtle	squirrel
lizard	alligator
lion	sidewinder
whale	monkey
rabbit	bear
black snake	king snake

mammals	birds

- -

kitten	falcon
dolphin	gorilla
parrot	robin
sparrow	koala bear
tiger	finch
eagle	parakeet
owl	fox
puppy	wolf
gopher	raven
dove	seagull

mammals	reptiles	birds

- -

panda bear	turtle
python	boa constrictor
stork	macaw
hawk	robin
garter snake	crane
cobra	flamingo
elk	antelope
kitten	polar bear
zebra	alligator
giraffe	whale

mammals	birds
reptiles	OUT OF SORTS

parrot	sparrow
grizzly bear	panda bear
hamster	kangaroo
fly	alligator
stork	owl
penguin	mouse
garter snake	hummingbird
eagle	skunk
worm	coral snake
bee	crocodile

have fur or hair	have feathers	have scales

---

goat	robin
lizard	alligator
parakeet	giraffe
crane	eagle
goose	turtle
cow	sparrow
dog	flamingo
king snake	cobra
panda bear	crocodile
raven	polar bear

have fur or hair	have scales
have feathers	OUT OF SORTS

gorilla	mackerel
rattlesnake	ant
lizard	shark
grasshopper	parrot
eagle	coral snake
spider	squirrel
bear	tuna
deer	crow
sparrow	flamingo
goldfish	hamster

forest dwellers	desert dwellers

deer	beaver
bighorn sheep	kangaroo rat
scorpion	prairie dog
rattlesnake	hawk
sidewinder	tarantula
bear	moose
squirrel	chipmunk
armadillo	wolverine
fox	roadrunner
wolf	elk

forest dwellers	desert dwellers	ocean dwellers

shark	beaver
deer	dolphin
eel	kangaroo rat
cactus wren	lobster
monkey	fox
parrot	bear
scorpion	wolf
jellyfish	tuna
sidewinder	desert tortoise
gorilla	whale

forest dwellers	ocean dwellers
desert dwellers	OUT OF SORTS

tuna	rattlesnake
roadrunner	fox
scorpion	book
crab	lobster
gray squirrel	clams
bicycle	wolf
shark	sidewinder
desert tortoise	kangaroo rat
bear	monkey
salmon	wagon

ocean words	forest words	desert words

seaweed	fish
cactus	shady
trees	many plants
surf	very hot
beach	seashells
oasis	many animals
sandy	dry weather
high tide	many shade trees
waves	low tide
few plants	lizards

ocean words	forest words
desert words	OUT OF SORTS

jellyfish	very hot
tarantula	waves
dry weather	deer
eraser	lizard
ferns	salt water
seaweed	monkey
beach	redwood tree
many trees	high tide
pine tree	pencil
cactus	desk

mammals	birds	amphibians

- -

deer	bear
skunk	cat
frog	tadpole
whale	owl
dog	parrot
canary	seagull
sparrow	pig
toad	newts
salamander	vulture
eagle	rabbit

mammals	fish
amphibians	birds

leopard	toad
goat	dog
frog	tadpole
crane	blackbird
whale	macaw
salamander	newt
angelfish	flounder
parakeet	tuna
skunk	hamster
shark	flamingo

mammals	birds

- -

have feathers	has fur
live births	hatch from eggs
lay eggs	may hibernate
most can fly	many fly south
have hair	warm-blooded
have beaks	grow up slowly
only have two feet	grow up quickly
feed babies milk	include humans
have two wings	bright feathers
nest in trees	have teeth

mammals	birds	fish

---

cold-blooded	live in water
have feathers	breathe with gills
have fur	have fins
have scales	have hair
live births	can only swim
lay eggs in nests	have 2 or 4 legs
lay eggs in water	can run and jump
have beaks	feed babies milk
only have two feet	have two wings
can fly	have no legs

mammals	OUT OF SORTS
birds	fish

live in water	can fly
frog	can only swim
newt	breathe with gills
have wings	have a gullet
have hair or fur	feed babies milk
have no teeth	lay eggs in water
have only two legs	lay eggs in nests
have no legs	have fins
most have four legs	have scales
have beaks	have feathers

reptiles	mammals	fish

---

warm-blooded	some tails can regrow
have gills	young grow slowly
lay eggs in water	live births
have legs	lay eggs on land
molt skin	have forked tongue
feed babies milk	have fur or hair
can only swim	don't like the cold
can't walk or run	some have shells
some slither	breathe with lungs
have fins	some have paws

mammals	OUT OF SORTS
reptiles	fish

teach their young	lay eggs in water
some have shells	lay eggs on land
molt skin	some brush teeth
live in oceans	warm-blooded
some have paws	have fur or hair
have wings	have fins
raise their young	don't have scales
gathers pollen	some have rattles
have gills	have feathers
some slither	can only fly

plant and animal terms	
plant terms	mammal terms

seedling	teeth
legs and paws	fossil
habitat	have fur or hair
germinate	environment
leaf	extinct
stem	sap
ears	flower
blood cells	nose
stomach	ecosystem
species	endangered

| plant terms | mammal terms |
| fish terms | reptile terms |

gills	leaf
stem	red blood cells
underwater	thorns
fins	cubs
live in desert	lay eggs in water
flower	seedling
fur	some have shells
scales	tail rattles
roots	milk for young
slithers	ears

forest ecosystem
desert ecosystem

- -

ponds	streams
pine cones	scorpions
sand dunes	cactus
lakes	many leaves
river	very dry
high temperatures	very moist
ferns	little rainfall
big leaves	many mammals
tall trees	rattlesnakes
conifer trees	tumbleweeds

water ecosystem

desert ecosystem

swamps	marshes
sand dunes	little rainfall
many plants	lakes and ponds
few plants	brackish water
many flowers	lizards
salt water	thorny plants
rivers	fresh water
cactus	very dry
few flowers	many ferns
many fish	tall trees

forest ecosystem	OUT OF
desert ecosystem	SORTS

sand dunes	rivers
streams	many flowers
cactus	rattlesnakes
department stores	tall trees
many trees	leafy plants
little rainfall	thorny plants
rivers	ice cream store
very hot weather	camels
football game	basketball
many mammals	beaver dams

herbivores (plant eaters)	carnivores (meat eaters)

mouse	butterfly
squirrel	blue whale
goat	beaver
wolf	wolverine
chicken	locust
fox	parakeet
rattlesnake	hyena
alligator	crocodile
eagle	bee
duck	sheep

herbivores (plant eaters)	OUT OF
carnivores (meat eaters)	SORTS

daisy	gray whale
alligator	wolf
sheep	gray fox
grasshopper	spider
buffalo	caterpillar
squirrel	prairie dog
cactus	deer
lion	moose
tiger	bumblebee
elm tree	pine tree

herbivores	carnivores	omnivores
(plant eaters)	(meat eaters)	(plant and meat eaters)

grasshopper	pig
wolf	squirrel
man	cow
rattlesnake	blue whale
killer whale	brown bear
woman	coyote
ladybug	boy
bumblebee	black bear
polar bear	spider
buffalo	caterpillar

herbivores (plant eaters)	carnivores (meat eaters)
omnivores (plant and meat eaters)	OUT OF SORTS

girl	pig
wolf	man
brown bear	woman
alligator	locust
rose bush	crocodile
bee	boy
caterpillar	tulip
grasshopper	sheep
ladybug	tree
goat	fox

the earth	the sun

- -

is made of gases	has glowing gases
surface is mostly water	has oceans
has people on it	rotates in 24 hours
has nine planets	does not turn at all
has comets	looks blue from outerspace
has oxygen	provides light for planets
has asteroids	has no water
has one moon	gives the moon light
has no moons	is always burning
is a star	has animals on it

| the earth | the moon |

- -

lunar	causes a lunar eclipse
rotates in 24 hours	orbits the sun
full phase	has glaciers
revolves around earth once a month	is a planet
travels 67,000 miles in an hour	has no seasons
crescent phase	orbits a planet
much of it is covered in water	has seasons
has no water	has oxygen
covered with dust and rocks	has no oxygen
has salt and fresh water	reflects the sun's light

the earth	the sun

- -

is a planet	casts shadows
is a star	is the larger of the two
is mostly water	has nine planets circling it
has no water	has one moon
rotates in 24 hours	is the center of the solar system
has seasons	meteorites hit it
is mostly gases	comets orbit it
is very, very hot	has life on it
has very cold areas	has very strong gravity
has oxygen	is between Venus and Mars

| our earth | other planet |

---

supports life on it	has only one moon
has the largest volcano on it	has no moons
is third from the sun	has 8 moons
has the hottest surface	is closest to the sun
is made of ice	is mostly covered in water
rotates in 24 hours	is covered with red dust
takes 6 days to revolve	has oxygen
has a large red spot	is made of frozen gases
is fourth from the sun	has many rings around it
tilts on its side as it revolves	takes 365 to orbit the sun

the earth	the sun
OUT OF SORTS	

plants grow on it	has continents
is the center of the solar system	is next to Mars
has one moon	full phase
has no moons	is a planet
is a star	has oxygen
covered with dust and rocks	orbits a planet
has very, very strong gravity	has a watery surface
lunar	has a very hot core
has salt water	is extremely hot
is made of glowing gases	planets orbit it

planets	stars

- -

form constellations	are very hot
orbit the sun	help sailors navigate
are made of gases	are like our sun
have moons	Jupiter is the largest one
have hot or cold surfaces	some are much larger than the sun
Pluto is the smallest	emit light
have comets	may have water
have asteroids	may have volcanoes
some shoot through the sky	there are millions of them
nine in our system	gravity holds them in orbit

| outer space | the sun |

- -

has many, many stars	is a star
has other solar systems	we have no idea how far it extends
nine planets orbit it	is the center of our solar system
reflects off moons	keeps Mars very hot
warms the planets	shines all of the time
has black holes	has small explosions called sunspots
has other galaxies	goes beyond the Milky Way
may have life we don't know about	supports life on Earth
distances measured in light years	is beyond our constellation
may hold other planets	is made of burning gases

plants	rocks and soils

- -

used for food	need sunlight to live
metals	harden into bricks
make gemstones	used to make roads
made when lava hardens	form seeds
made of animal and plant layers	produce fruits and flowers
form the earth's top layer	give off oxygen
worn down by ice and snow	make beautiful sculptures
need water to live	make gravel
a boulder is a large one	produce timber
the redwood is the tallest one	make adobe

plants	water

---

used to transport goods	used to make cloth
used as food	used for shade
used to make hydroelectricity	used for bathing
used for swimming	used to grow plants
used to make furniture	produce fruits and flowers
used for medicines	used for a campfire
used for cleaning	used to grow living things
used for drinking	makes paper
used to build houses	forms glaciers
used as heat for cooking	makes snow

plants	water

soils and rocks

- -

forms lakes and rivers	used to make jewelry
used to make bricks	some are valuable gemstones
used by animals for food	makes metals
used to grow plants	used for cleaning
used to make gravel roads	used for fuel
used for medicines	used for swimming
produce fruits and flowers	makes snowflakes
used to make hydropower	used to make cloth
used to make sculptures	used for windsurfing
plants grow in it	used for boating

minerals	rocks	plants

---

diamonds	limestone
slate	cactus
graphite	marble
sapphires	granite
emeralds	tulips
gold	tourmaline
sandstone	silicon
quartzite	palms
pumice	grass
ferns	rubies

metamorphic rocks	sedimentary rocks
igneous rocks	

pumice	hematite
sandstone	clay
quartzite	lava
marble	black sand
slate	changed by heat
hardened after melting	limestone
obsidian	was once melted
crystals	formed from layers
layers are squeezed together	has cooled off after melting
basalt	changed by heat and pressure

work with plants and the earth	work with animals and living things

florist	mineralogist
zoologist	geologist
botanist	dermatologist
pathologist	cytologist
geochemist	sociologist
horticulturist	psychologist
geophysicist	seismologist
herpetologist	physical therapist
entomologist	optometrist
anthropologist	audiologist

objects that sink	objects that float
ball	book
brick	boulder
driftwood	chair
boat	canoe
rock	logs
ferryboat	balloon
shell	can of corn
anchor	boot
basketball	lamp
shoe	football

light	heat

---

makes shadows	makes gases warmer
makes things warmer	moves in a straight line
lets us see	makes rainbows
makes liquids boil	melts ice cubes
changes liquids to gases	changes darkness
makes solids melt	reflects off mirrors
breaks into many colors	can burn you
electric bulbs brighten us	makes plants grow
cooks things	cannot be seen
bounces off solid objects	measured in degrees

solids	liquids

- -

have their own shape	can be small or very large in size
can be smooth or rough	form tidal waves
can be hard or soft	can be frozen
can be poured	can't be held in your open palm
forms rain	are wet
where fish live	flow quickly
take the shape of their containers	sometimes are lifted by a crane
can be heated to boiling	cover most of the earth
can flow	do not change shape
can be very dense and heavy	can be alive

solids	gases

---

don't change shape on their own	are used to fill balloon's
can be weighed in pounds	can be lifted by a crane
cannot be touched	take the shape of its container
have their own shape	can be measured by a ruler
can be invisible	can be rough or smooth
fills all the space in a container	some are very dangerous
can have an odor	can be soft or hard
the most common one on earth is air	most do not have an odor
some are lighter than air	can be poisonous or explosive
can be very dense	can be measured for length and width

liquids	gases

- -

cannot be seen	can quench a thirst
are wet	cannot be poured
most are odorless	cannot be felt
can be poured	can flow quickly
can be poisonous	can lift a kite
always fills all of a container's space	measured in liters or gallons
can be frozen	always run downhill
cannot be heard	can be seen and heard
melted ice	can make a balloon rise
cannot be held in an open container	can be held in an open container

| solids | liquids | gases |

- -

keeps their own shape	hard to find in a desert
cannot be seen	always fills all of a container's space
can be poured	flow quickly or slowly
can be weighed in pounds	has a texture
always run downhill	measured by a yardstick
do not have an odor	can be invisible and explosive
their length, width and height can be measured	can be soft or hard
measured in liters or gallons	makes up our air
do not have a color	needed if you are thirsty
fill most of the earth	can be boiled or frozen

solids	liquids

---

blocks of wood	milk
cola	plate
table	sponge
coffee	gasoline
tea	soda
chair	car
glass	truck
stove	orange juice
water	hammer
bathtub	computer

| solids | gases |

---

bus	hydrogen
oxygen	book
neon	radon
truck	butane
plane	basket
nitrogen	wagon
helium	television
argon	cup
desk	propane
lamp	bottle

solids	liquids	gases

- -

oxygen	steel
water	nitrogen
rock	neon
ice	soda
oil	ice cream
wood	argon
coal	steam
hydrogen	granite
juice	glass
milk	gasoline

solids	liquids	OUT OF SORTS

- -

oceans	tea
boat	yardstick
rivers	milk
oxygen	neon
helium	rocking chair
water	coffee
bricks	diamonds
soda	milkshake
pencil	rocks
ruler	air

solids	gases	OUT OF SORTS

- -

oxygen	methane
plane	skateboard
water	roller skates
argon	hydrogen
nitrogen	carbon dioxide
neon	truck
bus	butane
propane	paper
milk	tomato juice
surfboard	book

science skills	science tools

measure	ruler
microscope	spring scale
compare	thermometer
record data	investigate
barometer	magnifying glass
beaker	pencil
classify	identify
hypothesize	timer
infer	meterstick
balance scale	observe

science skills	science tools
OUT OF SORTS	

predict	baseball
timer	pencil and paper
beaker	balance scale
record data	classify
spring scale	microscope
hypothesize	question
thermometer	analyze data
observe	soccer
ruler	football
investigate	magnifying glass

oceans	continents

- -

have salty water	where people live
the largest pieces of land	have many ships on it
have countries on them	have submarines
have tidal waves	have highways
Europe	have whales and dolphins
form gulfs	contain lakes
form seas	have cars
the largest bodies of water	have airports
have rivers flowing through them	contain icebergs
contain towns	have seals

oceans	continents	OUT OF SORTS

Asia	Lake Erie
Great Salt Lake	Antarctica
Atlantic	Iraq
Europe	Yosemite
Jupiter	Arctic
Pacific	Australia
North America	New York
desert	Africa
Indian	California
South America	Antarctic

words about water	words about land
harbor	river
city	town
mountain	creek
tides	village
ocean	ship
valley	farm
lake	meadow
forest	suburb
hill	stream
sea	pond

words about water	words about land

country	river
sea	stream
lagoon	village
town	continent
pond	mountain
ocean	creek
city	hill
farm	desert
suburb	forest
lake	tides

words about water	words about land	OUT OF SORTS

continent	sea
ocean	sun
thunder	forest
town	hill
river	pond
lake	stream
suburb	star
mountain	factory
lightning	bay
road	lagoon

Atlantic Ocean	Pacific Ocean

- -

the biggest ocean	named for a sunken city
touches California	touches Europe
on the east coast of the United States	touches Maryland
the deepest ocean	touches Alaska
touches New York	touches Florida
on the west coast of the United States	Hawaii is there
its name means "peaceful"	Hudson River empties into it
the Columbia River empties into it	the Titanic sunk there
touches Oregon	Cuba is there
touches Maine	the Statue of Liberty is near

Atlantic Ocean	Pacific Ocean
Indian Ocean	Arctic Ocean

touches the east coast of the USA	is west of Africa
lies south of India	is the warmest ocean
is west of Australia	is mostly ice and icebergs
is north and east of Brazil	where Californians surf
is the largest ocean	has polar bears
Japan is in this ocean	has the Philippine Islands
Hawaii is in this ocean	Europe is south of this ocean
lies north of Norway	the Gulf of Mexico flows into this ocean
lies east of Asia	Alaska is south of this ocean
the Titanic is there	Pakistan is north of this ocean

Atlantic Ocean	Pacific Ocean
Indian Ocean	

- -

Statue of Liberty is near	touches the Mediterranean Sea
Asia is north of it	touches the Caribbean Sea
on Australia's east coast	touches the Gulf of Alaska
Newfoundland's fishing banks	off the west coast of Kenya
Hawaii is there	New Zealand is there
touches Africa's east coast	lies west of Columbia
lies south of Pakistan	the western end of the Panama Canal
Cuba is there	the eastern end of the Panama Canal
lies east of Siberia	Indonesia's west coast
touches the Arabian Sea	South America's west coast

oceans	seas
rivers	lakes

- -

a stream that flows across land	lakes and these are fresh water
a pool of water completely surrounded by land	in Utah it is salt water
usually flow north to south	some start from underground streams
don't flow from place to place	are the deepest bodies of water
contain the most fish	are the smallest bodies of water
usually end in another body of water	are a part of an ocean
are really a smaller ocean	the Mississippi is one of these
the largest bodies of water	the Mediterranean is one of these
five of these are in the middle of North America	Ontario is one of these
an ocean and these are always salt water	the Indian is one of these

oceans	seas
rivers	lakes

Pacific	Ganges
Great Salt	Nile
Mississippi	Baltic
Adriatic	Bering
Mediterranean	Erie
Ontario	Missouri
Arctic	Caribbean
Amazon	Superior
Atlantic	Hudson
Michigan	Indian

North America
South America

- -

Canada	Washington, DC
Chile	Colombia
Mississippi River	Gulf of Mexico
Mexico	Andes Mountains
Argentina	Rocky Mountains
United States	the equator is here
Brazil	north of equator
Amazon River	Arctic Ocean
Bolivia	close to Antarctica
Peru	California

Canada	Mexico

United States

Mississippi River	Mexico City
speak French and English	Washington, DC
called a "melting pot"	Ottawa
speak Spanish	provinces
north of the United States	fifty states
south of the United States	Newfoundland
touches the Arctic Circle	British Columbia
Hudson Bay	Aztecs
Great Lakes	maple leaf flag
Gulf of California	stars and stripes flag

North America	South America
Europe	Asia	Australia

kangaroos	Ganges River
United States	Hudson River
east of the Indian Ocean	Spain
Peru	the Alps
China	Amazon River
Canada	Mexico
Italy	Brazil
lies south of Asia	has the most people
Alaska	has the most countries
Siberia	its middle is the Outback

Europe	Asia

- -

touches the Atlantic Ocean	lies north of the Indian Ocean
touches the Pacific Ocean	India
touches the Indian Ocean	where Marco Polo sailed to
touches the Mediterranean Sea	where the Vikings sailed from
has more people	where Christopher Columbus was sailing to
has more land	Paris
Greece	Germany
has smallest country	the Alps
Italy	Korea
China	where Magellan sailed from

Africa	Australia

- -

the equator goes through it	one country here was started by slaves from America
koala bears	was settled by England
a continent and a country	lions and elephants
west of New Zealand	the slave trade to America started here
the Sahara Desert	their winter is North America's summer
its middle is a hot, dry desert	is closer to Antarctica
camels	the continent farther north
raises many sheep	the continent farther south
kangaroos	lies south of Europe
Canberra is its capital	lies south of Asia

North America	South America

---

contains three main countries	the Andes Mountains
United States	touches the Arctic Ocean
the equator runs through it	its largest river is the Amazon
has more countries in it	its largest river is the Mississippi
its largest country is Brazil	Canada is its largest country
the Tropic of Cancer	the Tropic of Capricorn
the Gulf of Mexico touches it	the Rocky Mountains
Chile is on its west coast	is close to Antarctica
Mexico to its south	Greenland is off its coast
Cuba is north of it	many Spanish speaking countries

North America	OUT OF SORTS

United States	Gulf of Mexico
Italy	the Great Lakes
Canada	Mississippi River
Mediterranean Sea	Columbia River
Tropic of Cancer	Bering Sea
the equator	Great Salt Lake
Mexico	Asia
Alaska	Australia
Arctic Ocean	Hudson River
Indian Ocean	Japan

stormy weather	nice weather

- -

black clouds	swimming
sunshine	no black clouds
rainy	thunderstorm
high winds	hurricane
warm temperatures	windows open
puffy, white clouds	picnics
icy	foggy and cold
snowy	snowstorm
sleet	tornado
camping	baseball

stormy weather	nice weather	OUT OF SORTS

hurricane	snow and ice
thermometer	rain and wind
tornado	sunshine
ice storm	slight breeze
calm winds	strong winds
thunder and lightning	yardstick
typhoon	ruler
warm temperatures	white clouds
clear, blue skies	black clouds
sleet	inch

| summer | winter |

---

ice storm	warm breezes
warm temperatures	ice skating
snowstorm	roller skating
sunny	mittens
hot and humid	shorts
sleet	heavy coats
swimming	sandals
baseball	blizzard
ice hockey	warm rain
icy, cold winds	warm boots

summer	winter

---

swimming parties	icicles
ice storm	cold winds
warm coats	picnics
shorts	Fourth of July
mittens	Christmas
snow skiing	ice cream cones
hurricanes	hot chocolate
blizzards	flowers blooming
bathing suits	snowman
warm breezes	baseball

spring	fall

---

flowers blooming	farmers planting
leaves falling	trees getting leaves
warm days	farmers harvesting
cool days	pumpkins
Halloween	baseball begins
Easter	summer is next
animal babies born	trees losing leaves
cold winds	football
warm rain	winter is next
leaves change color	summer is leaving

spring	fall

- -

leaves turning red	Easter
flowers blooming	school begins
farmers planting	cool days
pumpkins	warm days
crops harvested	leaves falling
baby lambs born	shorter days
cool, crisp nights	longer days
more sunshine	leaves budding
less sunshine	winter is next
Halloween	summer is next

producers	products

- -

eggs	crops
cow	ham
milk	cooked meal
farmer	corn
baker	tree
lettuce	apple tree
chef	lumber
bread	apples
cheese	dressmaker
pig	clothes

producers	products

---

factory	sports coat
milk	cow
tailor	chicken
pig	pears
lumber	ham
pork chops	tree
bread	pumpkin pie
eggs	pear tree
farmer	sheep
baker	wool

city	suburbs
farms	

- -

tall skyscrapers	many buses and taxi cabs
barns	malls
near a big city	horses
many homes with lawns	tractors
dairy cows	new homes
subways	pigs and goats
many people close together	small neighborhoods
has museums and zoos	commute to the city
crops	silos
many factories	buildings close together

city	suburbs
farms	OUT OF SORTS

traffic jams	stars
tall buildings	planted fields
cows and pigs	subways
sun	new homes
small neighborhoods	large crowds
barns and silos	crops to be picked
rivers	near a big city
commute to the city	open land
train station to the city	many cars and people
skyscrapers	night

the post office	the firehouse
the school	

---

firefighter	teacher
student	special delivery
letters in envelopes	pencils and crayons
postal worker	loud sirens
textbook	axe
fire engine	mail clerk
stamps	principal
brass pole for sliding	fire hose
mailboxes	reading teacher
fire hat	hook and ladder truck

the post office	the firehouse
the school	OUT OF SORTS

fire hose	subway
library	train tracks
stamps	principal
fire engine	mail carrier
teacher	fire hat
letters	airplane
student	house
mail clerk	school bus
mailboxes	textbook
desks and chairs	firefighter

the post office	the firehouse
the school	the library

- -

fire engine	student
librarian	mail carrier
check out books	money orders
mailboxes	loud sirens
stamps	textbook
teacher	playground
fire hat	recess
principal	mail clerk
overdue book notices	rooms of books
letters	learning centers

the police station	the shopping mall
the grocery store	

- -

frozen foods	book stores
criminals inside	guns and nightsticks
many different stores	fruit and vegetables
police cars	food court
milk and butter	jail
shoe stores	two-way radios
police badges	911 calls
toy store	bakery section
department stores	grocery clerks
grocery carts	lock up

the police station	the shopping mall
the grocery store	OUT OF SORTS

lock up	basketball court
sports stores	shoe stores
bakery section	book stores
cars with sirens	radio dispatchers
swimming pool	milk and butter
police badges	jail
handcuffs	many stores
department stores	911 calls
grocery carts	tennis court
fruit and vegetables	hospital

Native Americans of the Northwest	Native Americans of the Plains

made totem poles	finding food was easier
hunted buffalo	great woodworkers
fished daily	followed the buffalo
ate shellfish	were great horsemen
built cedar longhouses	had many arts and crafts
carved wooden masks	women carried heavy loads
farmed for food	were always moving to find food
used animal skins in many ways	lived in cedar houses with many families
lived in tepees on hunts	dried fish for winter
grew only a few crops	finding food and water was difficult

Native Americans of the Northwest	Native Americans of the Plains
Native Americans of the Southwest	

---

hunted buffalo	lived in cedar houses
were great fishermen	were nomadic hunters
made sand paintings	made beautiful jewelry
corn was the most important crop	were great horsemen
ate a lot of fish	lived in the deserts
lived in adobe mud houses	were shepherds
finding water was difficult	known for weaving blankets
made totem poles	lived on the prairies
lived in tepees	lived in the coastal forests
were weavers	made beautiful wood carvings

| Native Americans of the Northwest | Native Americans of the Plains |
| Native Americans of the Southwest | Native Americans of the Northeast |

great horsemen	one tribe was the Mohicans
weavers of blankets	made wooden canoes
ate a lot of fish	made bark canoes
used corn in many ways	made jewelry
depended on the buffalo	lived in buffalo skin tepees
lived in adobe mud houses	were shepherds
helped the Pilgrims	great wood carvers
made sand paintings	built the first apartment houses
hunted many forest animals	made totem poles
used buffalo skins in many ways	were nomadic hunters

English Settlers	Spanish Settlers

settled California	sent priests to convert the Native Americans
first came as Pilgrims	came for freedom of religion
sailed on the Mayflower	brought the horse to America
built many missions	held the first Thanksgiving
settled in New England first	began to move to the west to settle
moved north from Mexico	began to move to the north to settle
began the first college in America	explored Texas
settled the east coast	came from England
started schools for the Native Americans	loyal to the Spanish king
settled the west coast	built log cabins

English Settlers	Spanish Settlers
OUT OF SORTS	

---

sailed on the Mayflower	settled in Canada
settled California	named the Rio Grande River
first came as Pilgrims	named the Mississippi River
settled in New England first	started the first college in America
Native Americans helped them survive the first winter	came for freedom of religion
brought the horse to America	named New Orleans
named Los Angeles	built log cabins
held the first Thanksgiving	used adobe bricks
built many missions	settled the east coast
explored Texas	settled the west coast

the Spanish in America	the English in America
the French in America	

- -

came from England	named Plymouth
came to Mexico first	held the first Thanksgiving
sailed on the Mayflower	looked for the golden city
settled in Quebec	settled California
built many missions	built forts along the St. Lawrence River
settled in the northeast first	sold Louisiana to the United States
settled in the southwest first	named San Antonio
settled in Canada and Louisiana first	came for freedom of religion
named New Orleans	settled Texas
named San Francisco	began moving west from the east coast

East Coast Settlers	West Coast Settlers

---

endured harsh winters	some were called Pilgrims
settled in New England first	brought horses to America
came from Mexico first	established a highway from south to north
Father Serra traveled north	used logs to build their first homes
held the first Thanksgiving	named San Diego and San Francisco
the Native Americans helped them survive the first winter	their missions were one day's ride apart
tried to teach the Native Americans about their religion	used adobe to build shelters
first sailed on the Mayflower	kept close ties to England
set up many missions	kept close ties to Spain
began the first colleges	many died the first winter

East Coast Settlers	West Coast Settlers

OUT OF SORTS

- -

built many missions	settled in Kansas
lived in log cabins	their missions were one day's ride apart
lived in adobe buildings	began the first colleges
arrived on ships from England	tried to teach the Native Americans about their religion
some came looking for gold	were loyal to the Spanish king
settled in Ohio	came for religious freedom
endured cold, harsh winters	explored Texas
built settlements from the south to the north	brought horses to America
the Native Americans helped them survive the first winter	held the first Thanksgiving
named San Francisco and Los Angeles	came from England

nutritious foods	non-nutritious foods
apples	tomatoes
potato chips	oranges
celery	milk
carrots	chocolate syrup
candy bar	pears
cauliflower	cheese
french fries	cucumbers
lollipop	bubble gum
lettuce	cupcake
cake	donuts

non-nutritious foods	
nutritious foods	**OUT OF SORTS**

- -

lemons	grapefruit
knife	fork
chocolate bar	tomatoes
celery	chocolate cake
donuts	spoon
carrots	candy bar
lollipop	oranges
milk	sugar cookies
cucumbers	dish
lettuce	cottage cheese

fruits	vegetables

apples	pears
lettuce	onions
lemons	squash
tomatoes	potatoes
celery	limes
peaches	carrots
cabbage	grapefruit
grapes	peas
asparagus	green beans
oranges	cauliflower

fruits	vegetables

OUT OF SORTS

lemons	oranges
limes	broccoli
cabbage	milk
gum	grapes
pears	grapefruit
peaches	cherries
squash	cucumber
peas	carrots
cupcake	bread
apples	cauliflower

fruits	vegetables
sweets	

---

oranges	pears
sugar cookies	soda
cauliflower	bananas
lemons	spinach
squash	marshmallows
celery	lollipops
carrot	candy cane
peaches	pineapple
candy bar	apple
broccoli	lettuce

fruits	vegetables
sweets	OUT OF SORTS

asparagus	corn
lettuce	grapes
lemons	peas
peaches	pie
apples	oranges
cookies	eggs
milk	pears
spinach	carrots
candy	hot dog
bread	broccoli

healthy activities	unhealthy activities

jogging	eating candy
eating potato chips	playing football
eating a salad	roller skating
jumping rope	sitting all day
playing video games for hours	ice skating
eating vegetables	not exercising
watching TV for hours	dancing
playing basketball	eating many sweets
not sleeping	not eating breakfast
walking	playing baseball

healthy activities	unhealthy activities	OUT OF SORTS

---

playing softball	playing video games all day
eating candy	not sleeping
eating fruit	table
chair	sitting all day
jumping rope	getting sunburned
watching TV all day	playing ice hockey
eating vegetables	doing gymnastics
playing baseball	eating only sweets
running	lamp
roller skating	playing basketball

healthy habits	unhealthy habits
eating fruits	watching TV for hours
eating candy	jogging
eating only bread	playing soccer
drinking soda	sitting all day
eating vegetables	sleeping for 8 hours
drinking water	playing baseball
eating many cookies	eating fried foods
brushing teeth	jumping rope
flossing your teeth daily	eating junk food
exercising	not exercising

healthy habits	unhealthy habits
OUT OF SORTS	

playing basketball	walking daily
watching TV for hours	drinking water
elephant	drinking soda
eating fruits	giraffe
eating vegetables	sleeping for 8 hours
eating fried foods	panda bear
running daily	sitting all day
jumping rope	eating junk foods
zebra	drinking milk
eating lots of candy	playing soccer

respiratory system	circulatory system	skeletal system

heart	auricle
ribs	elbow
lungs	throat
veins	blood
nose	humerus
capillaries	spine
mouth	cranium
arteries	femur
bronchial tubes	kneecap
joints	ventricle

digestive system	nervous system	circulatory system

heart	neurons
stomach	enzymes
spinal cord	synapses
arteries	veins
esophagus	pancreas
nerves	ventricle
small intestine	nerve cells
blood	heart valves
brain	capillaries
large intestine	sense organs

digestive system	respiratory system
skeletal system	circulatory system

heart	arteries
lungs	nose
blood	heart valves
stomach	veins
bronchial tubes	femur
spine	pelvis
trachea	capillaries
small intestine	collarbone
ribs	joints
large intestine	elbow

digestive system	respiratory system
skeletal system	circulatory system

- -

lungs	pelvis
spine	diaphragm
esophagus	saliva glands
heart	arteries
blood	left ventricle
veins	nostrils
femur	joints
stomach	capillaries
nose	trachea
small intestine	wrist bone

| digestive system | respiratory system | OUT OF SORTS |
| skeletal system | circulatory system | |

---

veins	hat
pine tree	spine
stomach	saliva glands
lungs	nose
skull	arteries
esophagus	pelvis
capillaries	throat
napkins	small intestine
heart	right ventricle
diaphragm	ribs

muscular system	skeletal system	sense organs

pupil	retina
eardrum	optic nerve
femur	clavicle
fibula	deltoid
rib cage	spine
iris	triceps
ear canal	skull
flexors	tongue
biceps	quadriceps
pelvis	tibia

muscular system	skeletal system
sense organs	OUT OF SORTS

nose	clavicle
triceps	shirt
skull	bicep
shoe	ear canal
retina	quadriceps
tongue	eardrum
pants	iris
spine	pupil
rib cage	deltoid
fibula	flexors

shape names	number names

four	hexagon
triangle	nine
circle	pentagon
ten	parallelogram
one	two
square	oval
five	three
six	octagon
rectangle	seven
eight	zero

shape names	number names

OUT OF SORTS

- -

ten	hexagon
red	circle
square	pentagon
one	six
triangle	two
rectangle	parallelogram
blue	green
three	five
four	octagon
seven	yellow

less than ten	more than ten

- -

twelve	seventeen
one	fourteen
four	two
eighteen	five
seven	nineteen
eleven	eight
three	nine
six	fifteen
thirteen	sixteen
zero	twenty

less than ten	more than ten

OUT OF SORTS

fifteen	twelve
nine	four
three	two
eleven	eighteen
triangle	five
thirteen	circle
eight	nineteen
one	seven
sixteen	rectangle
square	fourteen

addition terms
subtraction terms

plus	all together
minus	how many more
less	how many less
more than	fewer
less than	take away
total	add
difference	subtract
sum	how many in all
in all	subtrahend
remainder	minuend

addition terms	subtraction terms	OUT OF SORTS

more than	subtract
time	how many more
plus	fewer
less than	take away
total	difference
minus	sum
less	dollar
all together	remainder
money	multiply
in all	how many in all

addition	subtraction

- -

1 + 1 =	8 - 3 =
2 + 5 =	9 - 2 =
7 - 3 =	3 - 2 =
4 + 2 =	4 + 3 =
9 - 6 =	5 + 3 =
4 + 5 =	6 - 1 =
5 - 2 =	6 + 3 =
1 + 3 =	8 - 1 =
4 + 4 =	4 - 3 =
5 - 1 =	1 + 4 =

addition	subtraction

$2 + 2 =$	$4 - 2 =$
$4 - 3 =$	$10 - 4 =$
$5 + 5 =$	$5 - 4 =$
$1 + 5 =$	$6 - 3 =$
$9 - 4 =$	$2 + 5 =$
$8 - 3 =$	$6 + 1 =$
$7 - 2 =$	$4 + 4 =$
$4 + 3 =$	$8 - 1 =$
$6 + 4 =$	$9 + 1 =$
$3 + 6 =$	$8 - 5 =$

addition	subtraction

OUT OF SORTS

$2 + 1 =$	$9 - 1 =$
$2 - 1 =$	$6 - 2 =$
$4 + 5 =$	10
$5 - 2 =$	$5 + 1 =$
$5 + 5 =$	2
$6 + 3 =$	$6 + 1 =$
$7 - 2 =$	$5 - 3 =$
4	$6 - 4 =$
$7 + 1 =$	$3 + 5 =$
8	$4 - 0 =$

addition	subtraction
	multiplication

$3 + 2 =$	$3 \times 5 =$
$5 \times 6 =$	$7 \times 3 =$
$4 + 3 =$	$9 \times 1 =$
$9 - 3 =$	$7 - 3 =$
$4 \times 3 =$	$8 + 2 =$
$5 + 2 =$	$5 + 6 =$
$10 - 4 =$	$9 - 4 =$
$12 - 3 =$	$6 \times 4 =$
$4 + 6 =$	$9 \times 9 =$
$3 \times 2 =$	$5 - 3 =$

sums up to 5	sums 6 to 10

2 + 2 =	4 + 4 =
5 + 2 =	3 + 1 =
5 + 4 =	6 + 3 =
3 + 3 =	4 + 5 =
4 + 1 =	0 + 4 =
3 + 2 =	1 + 6 =
2 + 1 =	7 + 2 =
4 + 3 =	8 + 1 =
1 + 3 =	9 + 1 =
2 + 5 =	2 + 4 =

less than ten	more than ten

- -

$7 + 4 =$	$7 + 7 =$
$8 + 8 =$	$2 + 2 =$
$6 + 6 =$	$9 + 2 =$
$3 + 4 =$	$3 + 5 =$
$6 + 7 =$	$5 + 4 =$
$4 + 8 =$	$3 + 6 =$
$3 + 3 =$	$7 + 6 =$
$2 + 5 =$	$8 + 5 =$
$7 + 7 =$	$4 + 9 =$
$1 + 10 =$	$6 + 1 =$

less than ten	more than ten

OUT OF SORTS

$2 + 2 =$	$7 + 6 =$
$11 + 1 =$	$3 + 3 =$
$3 + 4 =$	$6 + 9 =$
$5 + 6 =$	$7 + 7 =$
$9 + 9 =$	$5 + 5 =$
$10 + 0 =$	$6 + 4 =$
$6 + 6 =$	$1 + 9 =$
$4 + 4 =$	$9 + 8 =$
$4 + 5 =$	$8 + 3 =$
$4 + 2 =$	$5 + 2 =$

ten and below

eleven and above

---

3 + 5 =	15 - 6 =
18 - 9 =	9 + 5 =
6 + 7 =	13 - 4 =
5 - 3 =	5 + 7 =
5 + 6 =	8 + 3 =
4 + 5 =	3 + 9 =
13 - 5 =	15 - 3 =
7 + 7 =	16 - 6 =
17 - 8 =	3 + 7 =
5 + 9 =	14 - 5 =

ten and below

eleven and above

3 + 5 =	2 + 1 =
5 + 5 =	7 + 6 =
5 + 6 =	4 + 3 =
9 + 6 =	5 + 2 =
4 + 4 =	9 + 5 =
4 + 6 =	4 + 1 =
2 + 3 =	6 + 2 =
3 + 3 =	6 + 6 =
8 + 4 =	9 + 4 =
6 + 6 =	4 + 2 =

ten and below

eleven and above

$4 + 5 =$	$8 + 9 =$
$9 + 6 =$	$9 - 3 =$
$14 - 3 =$	$15 - 3 =$
$12 - 4 =$	$9 + 5 =$
$9 + 3 =$	$12 - 6 =$
$4 + 6 =$	$7 + 9 =$
$5 + 3 =$	$15 - 4 =$
$15 - 6 =$	$16 - 5 =$
$7 + 7 =$	$11 - 4 =$
$18 - 6 =$	$4 + 7 =$

| ten and below | OUT OF |
| eleven and above | SORTS |

3 + 4 =	5 + 5 =
12 - 6 =	15 - 3 =
triangle	9 + 2 =
4 + 6 =	14 - 3 =
12 - 4 =	4 + 5 =
9 + 4 =	11 - 3 =
2 + 6 =	square
8 + 9 =	5 + 6 =
16 - 7 =	plus
4 + 7 =	3 + 3 =

addition facts sums up to 10	addition facts sums 11 to 18
5 + 5 =	7 + 2 =
4 + 3 =	4 + 5 =
9 + 2 =	2 + 6 =
7 + 7 =	5 + 9 =
6 + 6 =	8 + 2 =
7 + 6 =	7 + 4 =
3 + 4 =	2 + 9 =
5 + 3 =	4 + 4 =
4 + 2 =	3 + 2 =
6 + 9 =	4 + 8 =

addition facts sums up to 10	addition facts sums 11 to 18
9 + 8 =	4 + 3 =
8 + 2 =	5 + 9 =
2 + 7 =	7 + 6 =
5 + 3 =	9 + 4 =
7 + 4 =	5 + 5 =
5 + 6 =	6 + 7 =
9 + 9 =	9 + 7 =
4 + 5 =	8 + 1 =
6 + 3 =	3 + 7 =
7 + 7 =	5 + 2 =

subtraction facts sums up to 5	subtraction facts sums 6 to 10
6 - 1 =	10 - 4 =
9 - 4 =	2 - 1 =
8 - 2 =	8 - 3 =
10 - 3 =	7 - 4 =
4 - 3 =	6 - 3 =
6 - 4 =	8 - 4 =
7 - 1 =	9 - 5 =
9 - 2 =	5 - 4 =
9 - 6 =	6 - 2 =
10 - 5 =	10 - 2 =

subtraction facts sums up to 5	subtraction facts sums 6 to 10

$10-4=$	$6-2=$
$8-2=$	$8-3=$
$6-4=$	$9-7=$
$7-3=$	$9-3=$
$9-2=$	$8-6=$
$7-5=$	$10-1=$
$10-5=$	$7-6=$
$7-4=$	$10-3=$
$6-1=$	$5-3=$
$4-3=$	$11-1=$

less than ten	more than ten
10-3 =	9+7 =
9+2 =	8-5 =
9-0 =	5+6 =
8-3 =	5+7 =
7+8 =	8-2 =
6+7 =	6+3 =
13-4 =	7+7 =
8+8 =	8+0 =
5-2 =	7+2 =
6-3 =	8+4 =

less than ten	more than ten

---

6 - 3 =	8 - 3 =
5 - 2 =	14 - 5 =
10 - 2 =	15 - 6 =
13 - 2 =	13 - 9 =
12 - 3 =	18 - 3 =
9 - 4 =	11 - 3 =
14 - 3 =	17 - 6 =
18 - 6 =	18 - 9 =
5 - 1 =	16 - 7 =
9 - 2 =	15 - 2 =

less than ten	more than ten

OUT OF SORTS

14-9 =	14-3 =
10-1 =	7-2 =
11-3 =	12-0 =
14-2 =	11+1 =
15-3 =	16-4 =
3+7 =	17-5 =
6-2 =	13-0 =
18-9 =	9-3 =
13-1 =	6-3 =
6-0 =	2+8 =

ten and below

eleven and above

---

3 - 2 =	14 - 1 =
9 - 3 =	16 - 4 =
18 - 6 =	15 - 7 =
12 - 1 =	17 - 5 =
9 - 6 =	15 - 4 =
13 - 5 =	14 - 9
14 - 2 =	17 - 6 =
15 - 3 =	19 - 1 =
8 - 4 =	9 - 5 =
7 - 3 =	11 - 6 =

subtraction facts differences up to 10	subtraction facts differences 11 to 18
18-9 =	14-3 =
7-4 =	8-5 =
16-5 =	12-7 =
12-4 =	13-8 =
11-2 =	18-3 =
17-6 =	15-6 =
16-4 =	16-9 =
13-5 =	15-9 =
14-5 =	12-1 =
17-8 =	9-5 =

subtraction facts differences up to 10	subtraction facts differences 11 to 18
$17 - 9 =$	$14 - 7 =$
$15 - 3 =$	$17 - 5 =$
$12 - 3 =$	$16 - 9 =$
$14 - 5 =$	$14 - 8 =$
$18 - 9 =$	$15 - 7 =$
$12 - 1 =$	$18 - 7 =$
$14 - 6 =$	$16 - 5 =$
$9 - 7 =$	$10 - 5 =$
$14 - 2 =$	$16 - 2 =$
$15 - 6 =$	$13 - 8 =$

time in hours only	time in hours and minutes
12:00	9:15
1:35	10:19
8:00	11:09
2:45	8:20
3:15	1:00
6:00	11:00
9:00	2:00
4:55	3:50
10:00	3:00
7:13	7:30

time in hours only	time in hours and minutes	OUT OF SORTS

1:30	1:15
5:00	6:00
2:00	1:00
200	425
5:15	4:18
7:10	345
8:30	11:15
9:00	10:00
610	12:16
12:00	8:00

after the hour	before the hour

10:15	9:23
10:35	11:50
12:01	8:32
9:10	7:55
11:05	4:33
7:12	1:10
6:22	11:45
9:45	5:14
6:10	10:10
5:46	3:43

after the hour	before the hour
on the hour	

- -

1:00	6:35
1:20	4:10
2:45	10:50
12:00	7:22
3:15	9:00
1:50	6:19
3:50	3:00
4:00	6:55
5:00	10:10
2:15	11:40

after the hour	before the hour
on the hour	OUT OF SORTS

5:05	1:00
3:35	3:45
10:10	9:32
4:00	2:25
125	5:10
4:15	459
345	6:25
12:00	7:45
5:15	9:00
632	10:00

money in coins	money in dollars

$.25	$.29
$1.00	$.50
$6.00	$.75
$.45	$9.00
$.35	$11.00
$.49	$.82
$8.00	$4.00
$.59	$7.00
$3.00	$2.00
$.63	$.99

money in coins	money in dollars
OUT OF SORTS	

$1.00	$.10
$.45	$10.00
$.50	$.05
$4.00	$.55
3:00	$3.00
$9.00	$.65
4:30	$2.00
$.75	$.39
$8.00	12:15
$7.00	$12.00

more than $10.00	less than $10.00
$1.25	$16.10
$12.25	$6.75
$11.35	$16.45
$4.50	$17.75
$9.50	$5.50
$3.35	$2.50
$7.25	$19.05
$15.00	$.65
$6.55	$.75
$13.45	$15.25

| money | time | shapes |

---

5 o'clock	rectangle
circle	7:25
$3.50	noon
6:30	hexagon
triangle	ten dollars
midnight	pentagon
two dollars	$5.50
square	12:10
$4.89	parallelogram
3:15	$15.20

Appendix

Learning Center Card

Directions for a
Closed Word Sort

Materials
word sort cards
category cards or "key word" cards

Directions
1. Place the word sort category cards or the "key word" cards at the top of the table.
2. Place the word sort cards on the table.
3. Think about the categories as you look carefully at each word sort card and say the word slowly.
4. Place the word sort card under the category it matches.
5. Sort all of the word cards this way.
6. If there are words that do not fit into any of the categories, place them in an "out of sorts" category.
7. Have someone check your sort.

plants	animals	OUT OF SORTS
daisy	deer	desk
fern	pig	
grass	tiger	

Directions for an
Open Word Sort

Materials
word sort cards
blank category cards

Directions
1. Place the word sort cards on the table.
2. Look carefully at all of the cards and say the words slowly.
3. Think about how some of the words might be alike.
4. Place those cards together and write how the words are alike on a blank category card. Place the category card above the words that fit in that category. Sort the rest of the word cards this way.
5. If there are any word sort cards that do not fit into any of the categories, make an "out of sorts" category card and place those word sort cards under it.
6. Have someone check your work.

the earth	the suns	out of sorts
has salt water	is a star	loves to read
has oxygen	is extremely hot	watches TV
has one moon	plants orbit it	

Answer Keys

#1
living things
cat
dog
fish
pig
cow
tree
hen
duck
snake
fox

non-living things
ball
hat
pen
rug
box
lamp
TV
desk
book
pin

#2
plants
tree
flower
rose
bush
daisy
grass
fern
fruit
seed
leaf
stem

animals
fox
dog
deer
chick
kitten
pig
puppy
cow
cat

#3
plants
daisy
tulip
cactus
shrub
fern
tree
grass
petunia

animals
deer
tiger
bear
squirrel
lion
fox
pig
beaver
hamster

Out of Sorts
bike
desk
computer

#4
belongs to plants
leaf
stem
branches
thorn
pollen
seed
flower
fruit
roots
petals

belongs to animals
fur
paws
teeth
nose
mouth
claws
ears
eyes
legs
heart

#5
parts of plants
seedling
stem
roots
branches
seed coat
flower
thorn
leaf
seed
pollen

parts of animals
head
eyes
paws
teeth
mouth
fur
ears
lungs
nose
stomach

#6
belongs to plants
leaf
seed
flower
stem
roots
branches
buds
seed coat
pollen

belongs to animals
nose
eyes
paws
tail
fur
ears
lungs
heart

Out of Sorts
door
window
roof

#7
vertebrates
dog
cat
parrot
whale
rattlesnake
tiger
bear
fox
elephant
frog

invertebrates
jellyfish
spider
shrimp
worm
bee
fly
crab
snail
squid
lobster

#8
vertebrates
snake
shark
wolf
dolphin
panda bear
cow
eagle
garter snake
horse
lion

invertebrates
bee
snail
earthworm
slug
spider
ticks

Out of Sorts
rock
flower
carrot
tree

#9
mammals
deer
elephant
camel
lion
whale
rabbit
dog
cat
squirrel
monkey
bear

reptiles
coral snake
turtle
lizard
black snake
rattlesnake
tree frog
alligator
sidewinder
king snake

#10
mammals
kitten
dolphin
tiger
puppy
gopher
gorilla
koala bear
fox
wolf

birds
parrot
sparrow
eagle
owl
dove
falcon
robin
finch
parakeet
raven
seagull

#11
mammals
panda bear
elk
kitten
zebra
giraffe
antelope
polar bear
whale

reptiles
python
garter snake
cobra
turtle
boa constrictor
alligator

birds
stork
hawk
macaw
robin
crane
flamingo

#12
mammals
grizzly bear
hamster
panda bear
kangaroo
mouse
skunk

reptiles
garter snake
alligator
coral snake
crocodile

birds
parrot
stork
penguin
eagle
sparrow
owl
hummingbird

Out of Sorts
fly
worm
bee

#13
have fur or hair
goat
cow
dog
panda bear
giraffe
polar bear

have feathers
parakeet
crane
goose
raven
robin
flamingo
eagle
sparrow

have scales
lizard
king snake
alligator
turtle
cobra snake
crocodile

#14
have fur or hair
gorilla
bear
deer
squirrel
hamster

have feathers
eagle
sparrow
parrot
flamingo
crow

have scales
rattlesnake
lizard
goldfish
mackerel
shark
coral snake
tuna

Out of Sorts
spider
ant
grasshopper

#15
forest dwellers
deer
bear
squirrel
fox
wolf
beaver
hawk
moose
elk
chipmunk
wolverine

desert dwellers
bighorn sheep
scorpion
rattlesnake
sidewinder
armadillo
kangaroo rat
prairie dog
tarantula
roadrunner

#16
forest dwellers
deer
monkey
parrot
gorilla
beaver
fox
bear
wolf

desert dwellers
cactus wren
scorpion
sidewinder
kangaroo rat
desert tortoise

ocean dwellers
shark
eel
jellyfish
dolphin
lobster
tuna
whale

#17
forest dwellers
gray squirrel
bear
fox
wolf
monkey

desert dwellers
roadrunner
scorpion
desert tortoise
rattlesnake
sidewinder
kangaroo rat

ocean dwellers
tuna
crab
shark
salmon
lobster
clams

Out of Sorts
bicycle
book
wagon

#18
ocean words
seaweed
surf
beach
high tide
waves
fish
seashells
low tide

forest words
trees
shady
many plants
many animals
many shade trees

desert words
cactus
oasis
sandy
few plants
very hot
lizards
dry weather

#19
ocean words
jellyfish
seaweed
beach
waves
salt water
high tide

forest words
ferns
many trees
pine tree
monkey
redwood tree
deer

desert words
tarantula
dry weather
cactus
very hot
lizard

Out of Sorts
eraser
pencil
desk

#20
mammals
deer
skunk
whale
dog
bear
cat
pig
rabbit

birds
canary
sparrow
eagle
seagull
vulture
owl
parrot

amphibians
frog
toad
salamander
tadpole
newt

#21
mammals
leopard
goat
whale
skunk
dog
hamster

fish
angelfish
shark
flounder
tuna

amphibians
frog
salamander
toad
tadpole
newt

birds
crane
parakeet
blackbird
macaw
flamingo

#22
mammals
live births
have hair
feed babies milk
have fur
may hibernate
warm-blooded
grow up slowly
include humans
have teeth

birds
have feathers
lay eggs
most can fly
have beaks
only have two feet
have two wings
nest in trees
hatch from eggs
many fly south
grow up quickly
bright feathers

#23
mammals
have fur
live births
have hair
feed babies milk
have 2 or 4 legs
can run and jump

birds
have feathers
have beaks
lay eggs in nests
only have two feet
can fly
have two wings

fish
cold-blooded
have scales
lay eggs in water
live in water
breathe with gills
have fins
can only swim
have no legs

#24
mammals
have fur or hair
have 2 or 4 legs
feed babies milk

birds
have wings
have no teeth
have only two legs
have beaks
can fly
lay eggs in nests
have feathers
have a gullet

fish
live in water
have no legs
can only swim
breathe with gills
lay eggs in water
have fins
have scales

Out of Sorts
frog
newt

#25
reptiles
molt skin
some slither
some tails can regrow
lays eggs on land
have forked tongue
some have shells
don't like the cold

fish
have gills
lay eggs in water
can only swim
can't walk or run
have fins

mammals
warm-blooded
have legs
feed babies milk
young grow slowly
breathe with lungs
live births
some have paws
have fur or hair

#26
reptiles
some have shells
molt skin
some slither
lay eggs on land
some have rattles

mammals
teach their young
some have paws
some brush teeth
warm-blooded
have fur or hair
don't have scales

fish
live in oceans
have gills
lay eggs in water
have fins
live in water

Out of Sorts
can only fly
have wings
have feathers
gathers pollen

#27
plant terms
seedling
germinate
leaf
stem
sap
flower

mammal terms
legs and paws
ears
blood cells
stomach
teeth
have fur or hair
nose

plant and animal terms
habitat
species
fossil
environment
ecosystem
endangered
extinct

#28
plant terms
stem
flower
roots
leaf
seedling
thorns

mammal terms
fur
red blood cells
cubs
milk for young
ears

fish Terms
gills
fins
lay eggs in water
underwater
scales

reptile terms
slithers
tail rattles
live in deserts
some have shells

#29
forest ecosystem
ponds
pine cones
lakes
rivers
ferns
big leaves
tall trees
conifer trees
streams
many leaves
very moist
many mammals

desert ecosystem
sand dunes
high temperatures
scorpions
cactus
very dry
little rainfall
rattlesnakes
tumbleweeds

#30
water ecosystem
swamps
many plants
many flowers
salt water
rivers
tall trees
many fish
marshes
lakes and ponds
brackish water
fresh water
many ferns

desert ecosystem
sand dunes
few plants
cactus
little rainfall
lizards
few flowers
thorny plants
very dry

#31
forest ecosystem
streams
many trees
rivers
many mammals
rivers
many flowers
tall trees
leafy plants
beaver dams

desert ecosystem
sand dunes
cactus
little rainfall
very hot weather
rattlesnakes
thorny plants
camels

Out of Sorts
department stores
football game
ice cream cone
basketball

#32
herbivores
mouse
squirrel
goat
chicken
duck
butterfly
blue whale
beaver
locust
parakeet
bee
sheep

carnivores
wolf
fox
rattlesnake
alligator
eagle
wolverine
hyena
crocodile

#33
herbivores
sheep
grasshopper
buffalo
squirrel
gray whale
caterpillar
prairie dog
deer
moose
bumblebee

Carnivores
alligator
wolf
gray fox
spider
lion
tiger

Out of Sorts
daisy
cactus
elm tree
pine tree

#34
herbivores
grasshopper
ladybug
bumblebee
buffalo
squirrel
cow
blue whale
caterpillar

carnivores
wolf
rattlesnake
killer whale
coyote
spider
polar bear

omnivores
man
woman
brown bear
boy
black bear
pig

#35
herbivores
bee
caterpillar
grasshopper
ladybug
goat
locust
sheep

carnivores
wolf
alligator
crocodile
fox

omnivores
girl
brown bear
man
woman
boy
pig

Out of Sorts
rose bush
tree
tulip

#36
the earth
surface is mostly water
has people on it
has oxygen
has one moon
has oceans
rotates in 24 hours
looks blue from outer space
has animals on it

the sun
is made of gases
has nine planets
has comets
has asteroids
has no moons
is a star
has glowing gases
does not turn at all
provides light for planets
has no water
gives the moon light
is always burning

#37
the earth
rotates in 24 hours
travels 67,000 miles in an hour
much of it is covered in water
has salt and fresh water
causes a lunar eclipse
orbits the sun
has glaciers
is a planet
has seasons
has oxygen

the moon
lunar
full phase
revolves around earth once a month
crescent phase
has no water
covered with dust and rocks
has no seasons
orbits a planet
has no oxygen
reflects the sun's light

#38
the earth
is a planet
is mostly water
rotates in 24 hours
has seasons
has very cold areas
has oxygen
has one moon
meteorites hit it
has life on it
is between Venus and Mars

the sun
is a star
has no water
is mostly gases
is very, very hot
casts shadows
is the larger of the two
has nine planets circling it
is the center of the solar system
comets orbit it
has very strong gravity

#39

our earth
supports life on it
is third from the sun
rotates in 24 hours
tilts on its side as it revolves
has only one moon
is mostly covered in water
has oxygen
takes 365 days to orbit the sun

other planets
has the largest volcano on it
has the hottest surface
is made of ice
takes 6 days to revolve
has a large red spot
is fourth from the sun
has no moons
has eight moons
is closest to the sun
is covered with red dust
is made of frozen gases
has many rings around it

#40

the earth
has one moon
has salt water
has continents
is next to Mars
is a planet
has oxygen
has a watery surface
has a very hot core
plants grow on it

the sun
is the center of the solar system
has no moons
is a star
is made of glowing gases
planets orbit it
is extremely hot
has very strong gravity

Out of Sorts
lunar
orbits a planet
full phase
covered with dust and rocks

#41

planets
orbit the sun
have moons
have hot or cold surfaces
nine in our system
Jupiter is the largest one
may have water
may have volcanoes
gravity holds them in orbit
Pluto is the smallest

stars
form constellations
are made of gases
have comets
have asteroids
are very hot
help sailors navigate
are like our sun
some are much larger than the sun
emit light
there are millions of them
some shoot through the sky

#42

outer space
has many, many stars
has other solar systems
has black holes
has other galaxies
may have life we don't know about
distances measured in light years
may hold other planets
we have no idea how far it extends
goes beyond the Milky Way
is beyond our constellation

the sun
nine planets orbit it
reflects off moons
warms the planets
is a star
keeps Mars very hot
is made of burning gases
shines all the time
has small explosions called sunspots
supports life on earth
is the center of our solar system

#43

plants
used for food
give off oxygen
need water to live
the redwood is the tallest one
need sunlight to live
form seeds
produce fruits and flowers
produce timber

rocks and soils
metals
make adobe
make gemstones
made when lava hardens
made of animal and plant layers
form the earth's top layer
worn down by ice and snow
a boulder is a large one
harden into bricks
used to make roads
make beautiful sculptures
make gravel

#44

plants
used as food
used to make furniture
used for medicines
used to build houses
used as heat for cooking
used to make cloth
used for shade
produce fruits and flowers
used for a campfire
makes paper

water
used to transport goods
used to make hydroelectricity
used for swimming
used for cleaning
used for drinking
used for bathing
used to grow plants
used to grow living things
forms glaciers
makes snow

#45

plants
used by animals for food
used for medicines
produce fruits and flowers
used for fuel
used to make cloth

soil and rocks
used to make bricks
used to make gravel roads
used to make sculptures
plants grow in it
used to make jewelry
some are valuable gemstones
makes metals

water
forms lakes and rivers
used to grow plants
used to make hydropower
used for cleaning
used for swimming
makes snowflakes
used for windsurfing
used for boating

#46

minerals
diamonds
sapphires
emeralds
rubies
tourmaline
gold

rocks
slate
graphite
marble
sandstone
quartzite
pumice
limestone
granite
silicon

plants
ferns
tulips
palms
grass
cactus

#47

metamorphic rocks
quartzite
marble
slate
crystals
changed by heat and pressure

sedimentary rocks
sandstone
black sand
clay
limestone
formed from layers
layers are squeezed together

igneous rocks
pumice
hardened after melting
obsidian
basalt
hematite
lava
changed by heat
was once melted
has cooled off after melting

#48

**work with plants
and the earth**
botanist
geochemist
mineralogist
geologist
seismologist
horticulturist
geophysicist
florist

**work with animals
and living things**
zoologist
pathologist
entomologist
herpetologist
physical therapist
anthropologist
dermatologist
cytologist
sociologist
audiologist
psychologist
optometrist

#49

objects that sink
brick
rock
shell
anchor
shoe
book
boulder
chair
can of corn
boot
lamp

objects that float
ball
driftwood
boat
ferryboat
basketball
canoe
logs
balloon
football

#50

light
makes shadows
lets us see
breaks into many colors
electric bulbs brighten us
bounces off solid objects
moves in a straight line
makes rainbows
changes darkness
makes plants grow
reflects off mirrors

heat
makes things warmer
makes liquids boil
changes liquids to gases
makes solids melt
cooks things
makes gases warmer
melts ice cubes
can burn you
cannot be seen
measured in degrees

#51

solids
have their own shape
can be smooth or rough
can be hard or soft
can be very dense and heavy
can be small or large in size
sometimes are lifted by a crane
do not change shape
can be alive

liquids
can be poured
where fish live
take the shape of their containers
can be heated to boiling
can flow
form waves
can be frozen
can't be held in your open palm
are wet
flow quickly
cover most of the earth
forms rain

#52

solids
don't change shape on their own
have their own shape
can be lifted by a crane
can be measured by a ruler
can be soft or hard
can be measured for length and width
can be very dense
can be rough or smooth
can be weighed in pounds

gases
cannot be touched
can be invisible
fills all the space in a container
can have an odor
the most common one on earth is air
some are lighter than air
are used to fill balloons
takes the shape of its container
some are very dangerous
most do not have an odor
can be poisonous or explosive

#53

liquids
are wet
can be poured
measured in liters or gallons
melted ice
can quench a thirst
can flow quickly
can be frozen
always run downhill
can be seen and heard
can be held in an open container

gases
cannot be seen
most are odorless
can be poisonous
always fills all of a container's space
cannot be heard
cannot be held in an open container
cannot be poured
cannot be felt
can lift a kite
can make a balloon rise

#54

solids
keep their own shape
can be weighed in pounds
their length, width and height
    can be measured
has a texture
can be measured by a yardstick
can be soft or hard

liquids
can be poured
always run downhill
measured in liters or gallons
fill most of the earth
hard to find in a desert
flow quickly or slowly
needed if you are thirsty
can be boiled or frozen

gases
cannot be seen
do not have an odor
do not have a color
always fills all of a container's space
can be invisible and explosive
makes up our air

#55

solids
blocks of wood
table
chair
glass
stove
bathtub
plate
sponge
car
truck
hammer
computer

liquids
cola
coffee
tea
water
milk
gasoline
soda
orange juice

#56

solids
bus
truck
basket
desk
lamp
book
plane
wagon
television
cup
bottle

gases
oxygen
neon
nitrogen
helium
argon
hydrogen
radon
butane
propane

#57

solids
rock
ice
wood
coal
steel
ice cream
granite
glass

liquids
water
oil
juice
milk
soda
gasoline

gases
oxygen
hydrogen
nitrogen
neon
argon
steam

#58

solids
boat
bricks
pencil
ruler
yardstick
rocking chair
diamonds
rocks

liquids
coffee
oceans
rivers
water
soda
tea
milk
milkshake

Out of Sorts
oxygen
helium
neon
air

#59

solids
plane
truck
bus
surfboard
skateboard
roller skates
paper
book

gases
oxygen
argon
nitrogen
neon
propane
methane
hydrogen
carbon dioxide
butane

Out of Sorts
water
milk
tomato juice

#60

science skills
measure
compare
record data
classify
hypothesize
infer
investigate
identify
observe

science tools
microscope
barometer
beaker
balance scale
ruler
spring scale
thermometer
magnifying glass
pencil
timer
meterstick

#61
science skills
predict
record data
hypothesize
observe
investigate
classify
question
analyze data

science tools
pencil and paper
beaker
spring scale
thermometer
ruler
timer
balance scale
microscope
magnifying glass

Out of Sorts
baseball
soccer
football

#62
oceans
have salty water
have tidal waves
form gulfs
form seas
the largest bodies of water
have many ships on it
have submarines
have whales and dolphins
contain icebergs
have seals

continents
the largest pieces of land
have countries on them
Europe
have rivers flowing
   through them
contain towns
where people live
have highways
contain lakes
have cars
have airports

#63
oceans
Atlantic
Pacific
Indian
Arctic
Antarctic

continents
Asia
Europe
North America
South America
Antarctica
Australia
Africa

Out of Sorts
Great Salt Lake
Lake Erie
Iraq
New York
California
Jupiter
desert
Yosemite

#64
words about water
harbor
tides
ocean
creek
sea
river
lake
ship
stream
pond

words about land
city
mountain
valley
forest
hill
town
village
farm
meadow
suburb

#65
words about water
sea
lagoon
pond
ocean
lake
river
stream
creek
tides

words about land
country
town
city
farm
suburb
village
continent
mountain
hill
desert
forest

#66
words about water
ocean
river
lake
sea
stream
bay
lagoon

words about land
continent
road
suburb
mountain
forest
hill
farm
valley

Out of Sorts
thunder
star
sun
lightning

#67
Atlantic Ocean
on the east coast of the United States
touches New York
touches Maine
named for a sunken city
touches Maryland
touches Florida
Hudson River empties into it
the Titanic sunk there
Cuba is there
the Statue of Liberty is near
touches Europe

Pacific Ocean
the biggest ocean
touches California
the deepest ocean
on the west coast of the United States
its name means "peaceful"
the Columbia River empties into it
touches Oregon
touches Alaska
Hawaii is there

#68
Atlantic Ocean
touches the east coast of the USA
is north and east of Brazil
the Titanic sunk there
is west of Africa
the Gulf of Mexico flows into this ocean

Pacific Ocean
is the largest ocean
Japan is in this ocean
Hawaii is in this ocean
lies east of Asia
where Californians surf
has the Philippine Islands

Indian Ocean
lies south of India
is west of Australia
Pakistan is north of this ocean
is the warmest ocean

Arctic Ocean
lies north of Norway
is mostly ice and icebergs
has polar bears
Europe is south of this ocean
Alaska is south of this ocean

#69

Atlantic Ocean
Statue of Liberty is near
Newfoundland's fishing banks
Cuba is there
touches the Mediterranean Sea
touches the Caribbean Sea
the eastern end of the Panama Canal

Pacific Ocean
on Australia's east coast
Hawaii is there
lies east of Siberia
touches the Gulf of Alaska
New Zealand is there
the western end of the Panama Canal
South America's west coast
lies west of Columbia

Indian Ocean
Asia is north of it
touches Africa's east coast
lies south of Pakistan
touches the Arabian Sea
Indonesia's west coast
off the west coast of Kenya

#70

oceans
the largest bodies of water
the deepest bodies of water
the Indian is one of these
contain the most fish

seas
are really a smaller ocean
an ocean and these are always salt water
are a part of an ocean
the Mediterranean is one of these

rivers
a stream that flows across land
usually flow north to south
some start from underground streams
the Mississippi is one of these
lakes and these are fresh water
usually end in another body of water

lakes
a pool of water completely surrounded by land
don't flow from place to place
five of these are in the middle of North America
in Utah it is salt water
are the smallest bodies of water
Ontario is one of these

#71

oceans
Pacific
Atlantic
Arctic
Indian

seas
Adriatic
Mediterranean
Baltic
Bering
Caribbean

rivers
Mississippi
Amazon
Ganges
Nile
Missouri
Hudson

lakes
Great Salt
Ontario
Michigan
Superior
Erie

#72

North America
Canada
Mississippi River
Mexico
United States
Washington, DC
Gulf of Mexico
Rocky Mountains
north of equator
Arctic Ocean
California

South America
Chile
Argentina
Brazil
Amazon River
Bolivia
Peru
Colombia
Andes Mountains
the equator is here
close to Antarctica

#73

Canada
speak French and English
north of the United States
touches the Arctic Circle
Hudson Bay
Ottawa
provinces
Newfoundland
British Columbia
maple leaf flag

United States
Mississippi River
called a "melting pot"
Great Lakes
Washington, DC
fifty states
stars and stripes flag

Mexico
speak Spanish
south of the United States
Gulf of California
Mexico City
Aztecs

#74

North America
United States
Canada
Alaska
Hudson River
Mexico

South America
Peru
Brazil
Amazon River

Europe
Italy
the Alps
has the most countries
Spain

Asia
east of the Indian Ocean
China
Ganges River
Siberia
has the most people

Australia
kangaroos
lies south of Asia
its middle is the Outback

#75

Europe
touches the Atlantic Ocean
touches the Mediterranean Sea
Greece
Italy
where the Vikings sailed from
has the smallest country
the Alps
where Magellan sailed from
Paris
Germany

Asia
touches the Pacific Ocean
touches the Indian Ocean
has more people
has more land
China
lies north of the Indian Ocean
India
where Marco Polo sailed to
where Christopher Columbus was sailing to
Korea

#76

Africa
the equator goes through it
the Sahara Desert
camels
one country here was started by slaves
    from America
lions and elephants
the slave trade to America started here
the continent farther north
lies south of Europe

Australia
koala bears
a continent and a country
west of New Zealand
its middle is a hot, dry desert
raises many sheep
kangaroos
Canberra is its capitol
was settled by England
is closer to Antarctica
the continent farther south
lies south of Asia
their winter is North America's summer

#77

North America
contains three main countries
United States
Tropic of Cancer
the Gulf of Mexico touches it
Mexico to its south
touches the Arctic Ocean
its largest river is the Mississippi
Canada is its largest country
Rocky Mountains
Greenland is off its coast

South America
the equator runs through it
has more countries in it
its largest country is Brazil
Chile is on its west coast
Cuba is north of it
the Andes Mountains
its largest river is the Amazon
the Tropic of Capricorn
is close to Antarctica
many Spanish speaking countries

#78

North America
United States
Canada
Tropic of Cancer
Mexico
Alaska
Arctic Ocean
Gulf of Mexico
the Great Lakes
Mississippi River
Columbia River
Bering Sea
Great Salt Lake
Hudson River

Out of Sorts
Italy
Mediterranean Sea
the equator
Indian Ocean
Asia
Australia
Japan

#79

stormy weather
black clouds
rainy
high winds
icy
snowy
sleet
thunderstorm
hurricane
foggy and cold
snowstorm
tornado

nice weather
sunshine
warm temperatures
puffy, white clouds
camping
swimming
no black clouds
windows open
baseball
picnics

#80

stormy weather
hurricane
tornado
ice storm
thunder and lightning
typhoon
sleet
snow and ice
rain and wind
strong winds
black clouds

nice weather
calm winds
warm temperatures
clear, blue skies
slight breeze
white clouds
sunshine

Out of Sorts
thermometer
yardstick
ruler
inch

#81

summer
warm temperatures
sunny
hot and humid
swimming
baseball
warm breezes
roller skating
shorts
sandals
warm rain

winter
ice storm
snowstorm
sleet
ice hockey
icy, cold winds
ice skating
mittens
heavy coats
blizzard
warm boots

#82
summer
swimming parties
shorts
bathing suits
warm breezes
picnics
Fourth of July
ice cream cones
flowers blooming
baseball
hurricanes

winter
ice storm
warm coats
mittens
snow skiing
blizzards
icicles
cold winds
Christmas
hot chocolate
snowman

#83
spring
flowers blooming
warm days
Easter
animal babies born
warm rain
farmers planting
trees getting leaves
baseball begins
summer is next

fall
leaves falling
cool days
Halloween
cold winds
leaves change color
farmers harvesting
pumpkins
trees losing leaves
football
winter is next
summer is leaving

#84
spring
flowers blooming
farmers planting
baby lambs born
more sunshine
Easter
warm days
longer days
leaves budding
summer is next

fall
leaves turning red
pumpkins
crops harvested
cool, crisp nights
less sunshine
Halloween
cool days
leaves falling
shorter days
winter is next
school begins

#85
producers
cow
farmer
baker
chef
pig
tree
apple tree
dressmaker

products
eggs
milk
lettuce
bread
cheese
crops
ham
cooked meal
corn
lumber
apples
clothes

#86
producers
factory
tailor
pig
farmer
baker
cow
chicken
tree
pear tree
sheep

products
milk
lumber
pork chops
bread
eggs
sports coat
pears
ham
pumpkin pie
wool

#87
city
tall skyscrapers
subways
many people close together
museums and zoos
many factories
many buses and taxi cabs
buildings close together

suburbs
near a big city
many homes with lawns
malls
small neighborhoods
commute to the city
new homes

farms
barns
dairy cows
crops
horses
tractors
pigs and goats
silos

#88
city
traffic jams
tall buildings
skyscrapers
subways
large crowds
many cars and many people

suburbs
small neighborhoods
commute to the city
near a big city
train station to the city
new homes

farms
cows and pigs
barns and silos
planted fields
crops to be picked
open land

OUT OF SORTS
sun
rivers
stars
night

#89
the post office
letters in envelopes
postal worker
stamps
mailboxes
special delivery
mail clerk

the firehouse
firefighter
fire engine
brass pole for sliding
fire hat
loud sirens
axe
fire hose
hook and ladder truck

the school
student
textbook
teacher
pencils and crayons
principal
reading teacher

#90
the post office
stamps
letters
mail clerk
mailboxes
mail carrier

the firehouse
fire hose
fire engine
fire hat
firefighter

the school
library
teacher
student
desks and chairs
principal
school bus
textbook

OUT OF SORTS
subway
train tracks
airplane
house

169

#91

the post office
stamps
letters
mail carrier
money orders
mail clerk
mailboxes

the school
teacher
principal
student
textbook
playground
recess
learning centers

the firehouse
fire engine
fire hat
loud sirens

the library
librarian
check out books
overdue book notices
rooms of books

#92

the police station
criminals inside
police cars
police badges
guns and nightsticks
jail
two-way radios
911 calls
lock up

the shopping mall
many different stores
shoe stores
department stores
toy store
book stores
food court

the grocery store
frozen foods
milk and butter
grocery carts
fruit and vegetables
bakery section
grocery clerks

#93

the police station
lock up
cars with sirens
police badges
radio dispatchers
911 calls
handcuffs
jail

the shopping mall
sports stores
department stores
shoe stores
book stores
many stores

the grocery store
bakery section
grocery carts
fruit and vegetables
milk and butter

Out of Sorts
swimming pool
tennis court
hospital
basketball court

#94

Native Americans of the Northwest
made totem poles
fished daily
ate shellfish
built cedar longhouses
carved wooden masks
farmed for food
finding food was easier
great woodworkers
had many arts and crafts
lived in cedar houses with many families
dried fish for winter

Native Americans of the Plains
hunted buffalo
used animal skins in many ways
lived in tepees on hunts
grew only a few crops
finding food and water was difficult
followed the buffalo
were great horsemen
women carried heavy loads
were always moving to find food

#95

Native Americans of the Northwest
lived in cedar houses
ate a lot of fish
made totem poles
lived in the coastal forests
made beautiful wood carvings
were great fishermen

Native Americans of the Plains
hunted buffalo
lived in tepees
were nomadic hunters
were great horsemen
lived on the prairies

Native Americans of the Southwest
made sand paintings
corn was the most important crop
lived in adobe mud houses
finding water was difficult
were weavers
made beautiful jewelry
lived in the deserts
were shepherds
known for weaving blankets

#96

Native Americans of the Northwest
ate a lot of fish
made wooden canoes
great wood carvers
made totem poles

Native Americans of the Plains
great horsemen
depended on the buffalo
used buffalo skins in many ways
lived in buffalo skin tepees
were nomadic hunters

Native Americans of the Southwest
weavers of blankets
used corn in many ways
lived in adobe mud houses
made sand paintings
made jewelry
were shepherds
built the first apartment houses

Native Americans of the Northeast
helped the Pilgrims
hunted many forest animals
one tribe was the Mohicans
made bark canoes

#97

English Settlers
first came as Pilgrims
sailed on the Mayflower
settled in New England first
began the first college in America
settled the east coast
came for freedom of religion
held the first Thanksgiving
began to move to the west to settle
came from England
built log cabins

Spanish Settlers
settled California
built many missions
moved north from Mexico
started schools for the Native Americans
settled the west coast
sent priests to convert
    the Native Americans
brought the horse to America
began to move to the north to settle
explored Texas
loyal to the Spanish king

#98

English Settlers
sailed on the Mayflower
first came as Pilgrims
settled in New England first
Native Americans helped them survive
    the first winter
held the first Thanksgiving
started the first college in America
came for freedom of religion
built log cabins
settled the east coast

Spanish Settlers
settled California
brought the horse to America
named Los Angeles
built many missions
explored Texas
named the Rio Grande River
used adobe bricks
settled the west coast

Out of Sorts
settled in Canada
named New Orleans
named the Mississippi River

#99

the Spanish in America
came to Mexico first
built many missions
settled in the southwest first
named San Francisco
looked for the golden city
settled California
named San Antonio
settled Texas

the English in America
came from England
sailed on the Mayflower
settled in the northeast first
named Plymouth
held the first Thanksgiving
came for freedom of religion
began moving west from the eat coast

the French in America
settled in Quebec
settled in Canada and Louisiana first
named New Orleans
built forts along the St. Lawrence River
sold Louisiana to the United States

#100

East Coast Settlers
endured harsh winters
settled in New England first
held the first Thanksgiving
Native Americans helped them
    survive the first winter
first sailed on the Mayflower
began the first colleges
some were called Pilgrims
used logs to build their first homes
kept close ties to England
many died the first winter

West Coast Settlers
came from Mexico first
Father Serra traveled north
tried to teach the Native Americans
    about their religion
set up many missions
brought horses to America
established a highway from
    south the north
name San Diego and San Francisco
their missions were one day's
    ride apart
used adobe to build shelters
kept close ties to Spain

#101

East Coast Settlers
lived in log cabins
arrived on ships from England
endured cold, harsh winters
the Native Americans helped them
    survive the first winter
began the first colleges
came for freedom of religion
held the first Thanksgiving
came from England

West Coast Settlers
built many missions
lived in adobe buildings
some came looking for gold
built settlements from the
    south to the north
named San Francisco
    and Los Angeles
their missions were one day's
    ride apart
tried to teach the Native Americans
    about their religion
were loyal to the Spanish king
brought horses to America

Out of Sorts
settled in Ohio
explored Texas
settled in Kansas

#102

nutritious foods
apples
celery
carrots
cauliflower
lettuce
tomatoes
oranges
milk
pears
cheese
cucumbers

non-nutritious foods
potato chips
candy bar
French fries
lollipop
cake
chocolate syrup
bubblegum
cupcake
donuts

#103

nutritious foods
lemons
celery
carrots
milk
cucumbers
lettuce
grapefruit
tomatoes
oranges
cottage cheese

non-nutritious foods
chocolate bar
donuts
lollipop
chocolate cake
candy bar
sugar cookies

Out of Sorts
fork
spoon
knife
dish

#104

fruits
apples
lemons
tomatoes
peaches
grapes
oranges
pears
limes
grapefruit

vegetables
lettuce
celery
cabbage
asparagus
onions
squash
potatoes
carrots
peas
green beans
cauliflower

#105
fruits
lemons
limes
pears
peaches
apples
oranges
grapes
grapefruit
cherries

vegetables
cabbage
squash
peas
broccoli
cucumber
carrots
cauliflower

Out of Sorts
milk
bread
gum
cupcake

#106
fruits
oranges
lemons
peaches
pears
bananas
pineapple
apple

vegetables
cauliflower
squash
celery
carrot
broccoli
spinach
lettuce

sweets
sugar cookies
candy bar
soda
marshmallows
lollipops
candy cane

#107
fruits
lemons
peaches
apples
grapes
oranges
pears

vegetables
asparagus
lettuce
spinach
corn
peas
carrots
broccoli

sweets
cookies
candy
pie

Out of Sorts
milk
bread
eggs
hot dog

#108
healthy activities
jogging
eating a salad
jumping rope
playing basketball
walking
playing football
roller skating
ice skating
dancing
playing baseball
eating vegetables

unhealthy activities
eating potato chips
playing video games
    for hours
watching TV for hours
not sleeping
eating candy
sitting all day
not exercising
eating many sweets
not eating breakfast

#109
healthy activities
playing softball
eating fruit
jumping rope
eating vegetables
playing baseball
running
roller skating
playing ice hockey
doing gymnastics
playing basketball

unhealthy activities
eating candy
watching TV all day
playing video games all day
not sleeping
sitting all day
getting sunburned
eating only sweets

Out of Sorts
chair
table
lamp

#110
healthy habits
eating fruits
eating vegetables
drinking water
brushing teeth
flossing your teeth daily
exercising
jogging
playing soccer
sleeping for 8 hours
playing baseball
jumping rope

unhealthy habits
eating candy
eating only bread
drinking soda
eating many cookies
watching TV for hours
sitting all day
eating fried foods
eating junk food
not exercising

#111
healthy habits
playing basketball
eating fruits
eating vegetables
running daily
jumping rope
walking daily
drinking water
sleeping for 8 hours
drinking milk
playing soccer

unhealthy habits
watching TV for hours
eating fried foods
eating lots of candy
drinking soda
sitting all day
eating junk foods

Out of Sorts
elephant
zebra
panda bear
giraffe

#112
respiratory system
lungs
nose
mouth
bronchial tubes
throat

circulatory system
heart
veins
capillaries
arteries
auricle
blood
ventricle

skeletal system
ribs
joints
elbow
humerus
spine
cranium
femur
kneecap

#113
digestive system
stomach
esophagus
small intestine
large intestine
enzymes
pancreas

nervous system
spinal cord
nerves
brain
neurons
synapses
nerve cells
sense organs

circulatory system
heart
arteries
blood
veins
ventricle
heart valves
capillaries

#114
digestive system
stomach
small intestine
large intestine

respiratory System
lungs
bronchial tubes
trachea
nose

skeletal system
spine
ribs
femur
pelvis
collarbone
joints
elbow

circulatory system
heart
blood
arteries
heart valves
veins
capillaries

#115

digestive system
esophagus
stomach
small intestine
saliva glands

respiratory system
lungs
nose
diaphragm
nostrils
trachea

skeletal system
spine
femur
pelvis
joints
wrist bone

circulatory system
heart
blood
veins
arteries
left ventricle
capillaries

#116

digestive system
stomach
esophagus
saliva glands
small intestine

respiratory system
lungs
diaphragm
throat
nose

skeletal system
spine
pelvis
ribs
skull

circulatory system
veins
capillaries
heart
arteries
right ventricle

Out of Sorts
pine tree
napkins
hat

#117

muscular system
flexors
biceps
deltoid
triceps
quadriceps

skeletal system
femur
fibula
rib cage
pelvis
clavicle
skull
tibia
spine

sense organs
pupil
eardrum
iris
ear canal
retina
optic nerve
tongue

#118

muscular system
triceps
quadriceps
flexors
bicep
deltoid

skeletal system
skull
spine
rib cage
fibula
clavicle

sense organs
nose
retina
tongue
ear canal
ear drum
iris
pupil

Out of Sorts
shoe
pants
shirt

#119

shape names
triangle
circle
square
rectangle
hexagon
pentagon
parallelogram
oval
octagon

number names
four
ten
one
five
six
eight
nine
two
three
seven
zero

#120

shape names
square
triangle
rectangle
hexagon
circle
pentagon
parallelogram
octagon

number names
ten
one
three
four
seven
six
two
five

Out of Sorts
red
blue
green
yellow

#121

addition
2+1=
4+5=
5+5=
6+3=
7+1=
5+1=
6+1=
3+5=

subtraction
2-1=
5-2=
7-2=
9-1=
6-2=
5-3=
6-4=
4-0=

Out Of Sorts
4
8
10
2

#122

less than ten
nine
three
eight
one
four
two
five
seven

more than ten
fifteen
eleven
thirteen
sixteen
twelve
eighteen
nineteen
fourteen

Out of Sorts
triangle
circle
square
rectangle

#123

addition terms
plus
total
sum
in all
all together
add
how many in all

subtraction terms
minus
less
more than
less than
difference
remainder
how many more
how many less
fewer
take away
subtract
subtrahend
minuend

#124

addition terms
plus
total
all together
in all
sum
how many in all

subtraction terms
more than
less than
minus
less
subtract
how many more
fewer
take away
difference
remainder

Out of Sorts
time
money
dollar
multiply

#125

addition
1+1=
2+5=
4+2=
4+5=
1+3=
4+4=
4+3=
5+3=
6+3=
1+4=

subtraction
7-3=
9-6=
5-2=
5-1=
8-3=
9-2=
3-2=
6-1=
8-1=
4-3=

#126	#127	#128	#129	#130	#131
addition	**less than ten**	**addition**	**sums to 5**	**less than ten**	**less than ten**
2+2=	one	3+2=	2+2=	3+4=	2+2=
5+5=	four	4+3=	4+1=	3+3=	3+4=
1+5=	seven	5+2=	3+2=	2+5=	4+4=
4+3=	three	4+6=	2+1=	2+2=	4+5=
6+4=	six	8+2=	1+3=	3+5=	4+2=
3+6=	zero	5+6=	3+1=	5+4=	3+3=
2+5=	two		0+4=	3+6=	5+2=
6+1=	five	**subtraction**		6+1=	
4+4=	eight	9-3=	**sums 6 to 10**		**more than ten**
9+1=	nine	10-4=	5+2=	**more than ten**	11+1=
		12-3=	5+4=	7+4=	5+6=
subtraction	**more than ten**	7-3=	3+3=	9+2=	9+9=
4-3=	twelve	9-4=	4+3=	8+8=	6+6=
9-4=	eighteen	5-3=	2+5=	7+7=	7+6=
8-3=	eleven		4+4=	6+6=	6+9=
7-2=	thirteen	**multiplication**	6+3=	6+7=	7+7=
4-2=	seventeen	5x6=	4+5=	4+8=	9+8=
10-4=	fourteen	4x3=	1+6=	1+10=	8+3=
5-4=	nineteen	3x2=	7+2=	7+7=	
6-3=	fifteen	3x5=	8+1=	7+6=	**Out of Sorts**
8-1=	sixteen	7x3=	9+1=	8+5=	10+0=
8-5=	twenty	9x1=	2+4=	4+9=	5+5=
		6x4=			6+4=
		9x9=			1+9=

#132	#133	#134	#135	#136	#137
ten and below	**ten and below**	**ten and below**	**ten and below**	**sums to 10**	**sums to 10**
3+5=	3+5=	4+5=	3+4=	5+5=	8+2=
18-9=	5+5=	12-4=	12-6=	4+3=	2+7=
5-3=	4+4=	4+6=	4+6=	3+4=	5+3=
4+5=	4+6=	5+3=	12-4=	5+3=	4+5=
13-5=	2+3=	15-6=	2+6=	4+2=	6+3=
17-8=	3+3=	9-3=	16-7=	7+2=	4+3=
15-6=	2+1=	12-6=	5+5=	4+5=	5+5=
13-4=	4+3=	11-4=	4+5=	2+6=	8+1=
16-6=	5+2=		11-3=	8+2=	3+7=
3+7=	4+1=	**eleven and above**	3+3=	4+4=	5+2=
14-5=	6+2=	9+6=		3+2=	
	4+2=	14-3=	**eleven and above**		**sums 11 to 18**
eleven and above		9+3=	9+4=	**sums 11 to 18**	9+8=
6+7=	**eleven and above**	7+7=	8+9=	9+2=	7+4=
5+6=	5+6=	18-6=	4+7=	7+7=	5+6=
7+7=	9+6=	8+9=	15-3=	6+6=	9+9=
5+9=	8+4=	15-3=	9+2=	7+6=	7+7=
9+5=	6+6=	9+5=	14-3=	6+9=	5+9=
5+7=	7+6=	7+9=	5+6=	5+9=	7+6=
8+3=	9+5=	15-4=		7+4=	9+4=
3+9=	6+6=	16-5=	**Out of Sorts**	2+9=	6+7=
15-3=	9+4=	4+7=	triangle	4+8=	9+7=
			square		
			plus		

#138	#139	#140	#141	#142
differences to 5	**differences to 5**	**less than ten**	**less than ten**	**less than ten**
6-1=	7-3=	10-3=	6-3=	14-9=
9-4=	7-5=	9-0=	5-2=	10-1=
4-3=	10-5=	8-3=	10-2=	11-3=
6-4=	7-4=	13-4=	12-3=	6-2=
9-6=	6-4=	5-2=	9-4=	18-9=
10-5=	6-1=	6-3=	5-1=	6-0=
2-1=	4-3=	8-5=	9-2=	7-2=
8-3=	6-2=	8-2=	8-3=	9-3=
7-4=	8-3=	6+3=	14-5=	6-3=
6-3=	9-7=	8+0=	15-6=	
8-4=	8-6=	7+2=	13-9=	**more than ten**
9-5=	5-3=		11-3=	14-2=
5-4=	7-6=	**more than ten**	18-9=	15-3=
6-2=		9+2=	16-7=	13-1=
	differences 6 to 10	7+8=		14-3=
differences 6 to 10	10-4=	6+7=	**more than ten**	12-0=
8-2=	8-2=	8+8=	13-2=	16-4=
10-3=	9-2=	9+7=	14-3=	17-5=
7-1=	9-3=	5+6=	18-6=	13-0=
9-2=	10-1=	5+7=	18-3=	
10-4=	10-3=	7+7=	17-6=	**Out of Sorts**
10-2=	11-1=	8+4=	15-2=	3+7=
				11-1=
				2+8=

#143	#144	#145	#146	#147
ten and	**differences to 10**	**differences to 10**	**time in**	**time in**
below	18-9=	17-9=	**hours only**	**hours only**
3-2=	7-4=	12-3=	12:00	5:00
9-3=	12-4=	14-5=	8:00	2:00
9-6=	11-2=	18-9=	6:00	9:00
13-5=	13-5=	14-6=	9:00	12:00
8-4=	14-5=	9-7=	10:00	6:00
7-3=	17-8=	15-6=	1:00	1:00
15-7=	8-5=	14-7=	11:00	10:00
14-9=	12-7=	16-9=	2:00	8:00
9-5=	13-8=	14-8=	3:00	
11-6=	15-6=	15-7=		**time in hours**
	16-9=	10-5=	**time in hours**	**and minutes**
eleven	15-9=	13-8=	**and minutes**	1:30
and above	9-5=		1:35	5:15
18-6=		**differences 11 to**	2:45	7:10
12-1=	**differences 11 to 18**	**18**	3:15	8:30
14-2=	16-5=	12-1=	4:55	1:15
15-3=	17-6=	17-5=	7:13	4:18
14-1=	16-4=	16-2=	9:15	11:15
16-4=	14-3=	15-3=	10:19	12:16
17-5=	18-3=	18-7=	11:09	
15-4=	12-1=	16-5=	8:20	**Out of Sorts**
17-6=		14-2=	3:50	200
19-1=			7:30	610
				425
				345

#148
after the hour
10:15
12:01
9:10
11:05
7:12
6:22
6:10
9:23
1:10
5:14
10:10

before the hour
10:35
9:45
5:46
11:50
8:32
7:55
4:33
11:45
3:43

#149
after the hour
1:20
3:15
2:15
4:10
7:22
6:19
10:10

before the hour
2:45
1:50
3:50
6:35
10:50
6:55
11:40

on the hour
1:00
12:00
4:00
5:00
9:00
3:00

#150
after the hour
5:05
10:10
4:15
5:15
2:25
5:10
6:25

before the hour
3:35
3:45
7:45
9:32

on the hour
4:00
12:00
1:00
9:00
10:00

Out of Sorts
125
345
632
459

#151
money in coins
$.25
$.45
$.35
$.49
$.59
$.63
$.29
$.50
$.75
$.82
$.99

money in dollars
$1.00
$6.00
$7.00
$3.00
$9.00
$11.00
$4.00
$8.00
$2.00

#152
money in coins
$.45
$.50
$.75
$.10
$.05
$.55
$.65
$.39

money in dollars
$1.00
$4.00
$9.00
$8.00
$7.00
$10.00
$3.00
$2.00
$12.00

Out of Sorts
3:00
4:30
12:15

#153
more than $10.00
$12.25
$11.35
$15.00
$13.45
$16.10
$16.45
$17.75
$19.05
$15.25

less than $10.00
$1.25
$4.50
$9.50
$3.35
$7.25
$6.55
$6.75
$5.50
$2.50
$.65
$.75

#154
money
$3.50
two dollars
$4.89
ten dollars
$5.50
$15.20

time
5 o'clock
6:30
midnight
3:15
7:25
noon
12:10

shapes
circle
triangle
square
rectangle
hexagon
pentagon
parallelogram